The KINGS TREASURIES
OF LITERATURE

GENERAL EDITOR
Sir A·T·QUILLER COUCH

JOHN BUNYAN

LONDON : J·M·DENT & SONS LTD.

JOHN BUNYAN

BUNYAN'S PILGRIM'S PROGRESS

ABRIDGED AND
EDITED BY
MARGARET A·GILLILAND
M·A·

THE lamented death of Miss Margaret Gilliland, while this edition of *The Pilgrim's Progress* was in the press, seems to call for a little explanation of the genesis of the book, which constitutes her last piece of work for the children she loved so well. Her advice was asked when the "Kings' Treasuries" were being planned, and at a time when she was seeking health to take up her work again. The plan of the series roused her enthusiasm at once, and she wrote: "You made me more than ever heart-sick for my children. I wanted to rush off and give some literature lessons straight away." She offered much excellent advice and suggested many suitable titles, and was especially anxious to prepare for younger pupils an edition of Bunyan's great work which would give the adventurous story without the excursions into Puritan theology or the frequent Bible references which so often distract the attention of a less mature reader. Her offer to prepare this book was gladly accepted and the present volume is the result. The proofs were

revised by another hand, but care was taken to present her book as she sent it to the publishers. The only addition made was the insertion of the headings which may help the reader to refer more readily to the various parts of the story; it is almost certain that Miss Gilliland would have approved of this slight modification in the interests of " my children."

May I be permitted to add a personal note, and to offer my homage to the memory of a teacher of the young whose lofty ideals and high enthusiasm ennobled all with whom she came in contact.

J. M. D.

THE ILLUSTRATIONS of this edition are worthy of special attention. They are carefully reproduced from the wonderfully imaginative cartoons of David Scott, R.A., and not only enhance the volume, but help in a very real way to interpret the spirit of Bunyan's immortal work. It is suggested that the attention of pupils be specially drawn to these pictures, every detail of which is worthy of careful study.

The Pilgrim's Progress is an allegory, that is, it has an interest over and above the story interest. A parable is a story of this kind, only it is very short and has not many incidents, while an allegory is worked out in detail.

Pilgrim's Progress is full of adventures, and you would expect it to be, because it is the record of a perilous journey from the City of Destruction to the Celestial City. When he wrote it in 1675–6 John Bunyan was in prison for conscience sake, but he saw in his mind the roads of Bedfordshire which he knew so well (by trade he was a travelling brazier) and he pictured adventures some of which might well have happened on these very roads. For those were the days when roads were lonely and highwaymen were pretty frequent. Then, too, he had read old tales of giants and of fights with fiery dragons, and he had himself, when a boy of sixteen, joined the Parliamentary Army, and knew from actual practice what warfare was like. The book also pictures a good deal of the every-day life of the time. Bunyan describes a Fair with its booths and shows, and the people whom his hero meets are very real. As the story goes on we come to

feel as if we really had met the characters in it, and we are quite sure that Bunyan knew them intimately. He makes us see the daily life of ordinary men in Puritan England in the seventeenth century.

But *Pilgrim's Progress* has an interest greater than this. It is the story of an adventure that is entered upon by each one of us who believes that his life is not given him merely for ease and pleasure, but for the realisation of ideals of high endeavour and noble service. You are, if you choose, the hero of the book. You can read in Christian's struggle against difficulty and danger, the record of your own attempts to make real to-day something of the ambition and noble purpose that thrill you when you think of the future and your work in the world. Like him, you can overcome robbers by the way. Like him, you can achieve the great adventure of your life, and find that happiness comes through self-conquest, and that only by way of the Hill Difficulty can you come to the Palace Beautiful.

CONTENTS

THE PILGRIM'S PROGRESS

LIST OF ILLUSTRATIONS

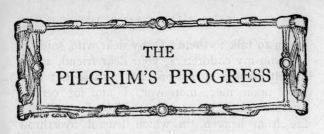

THE PILGRIM'S PROGRESS

CHRISTIAN LEAVES THE CITY OF DESTRUCTION

As I walked through the wilderness of this world, I lighted on a certain place where was a Den, and I laid me down in that place to sleep: and, as I slept, I dreamed a dream. I dreamed, and behold I saw a man clothed with rags, standing in a certain place, with his face from his own house, a book in his hand, and a great burden upon his back. I looked, and saw him open the book and read therein; and, as he read, he wept, and trembled; and not being able longer to contain, he brake out with a lamentable cry, saying, " What shall I do? "

In this plight, therefore, he went home and refrained himself as long as he could, that his wife and children should not perceive his distress; but he could not be silent long, because that his trouble increased. Wherefore at length he brake his mind to his wife and children; and thus he

Den. His own prison.
Man clothed with rags. Bunyan himself.

began to talk to them. O my dear wife, said he,
and you my children, I, your dear friend, am in
myself undone by reason of a burden that lieth
hard upon me; moreover, I am for certain
informed that this our city will be burned with
fire from heaven, in which fearful overthrow
both myself, with thee, my wife, and you my
sweet babes, shall miserably come to ruin, except
(the which yet I see not) some way of escape can
be found, whereby we may be delivered. At this
his relations were sore amazed; not for that
they believed that what he had said to them was
true, but because they thought that some frenzy
distemper had got into his head; therefore, it
drawing towards night, and they hoping that
sleep might settle his brains, with all haste they
got him to bed. But the night was as troublesome
to him as the day; wherefore, instead of sleeping,
he spent it in sighs and tears. So, when the
morning was come, they would know how he did.
He told them, Worse and worse: he also set to
talking to them again: but they began to be
hardened. They also thought to drive away his
distemper by harsh and surly carriages to him;
sometimes they would deride, sometimes they
would chide, and sometimes they would quite
neglect him. Wherefore he began to retire himself
to his chamber, to pray for and pity them, and
also to condole his own misery; he would also

walk solitarily in the fields, sometimes reading, and sometimes praying: and thus for some days he spent his time.

Now, I saw, upon a time, when he was walking in the fields, that he was, as he was wont, reading in his book, and greatly distressed in his mind; and as he read, he burst out, as he had done before, crying, " What shall I do to be saved? "

I saw also that he looked this way and that way, as if he would run; yet he stood still, because, as I perceived, he could not tell which way to go. I looked then, and saw a man named Evangelist coming to him, who asked, Wherefore dost thou cry?

He answered, Sir, I perceive by the book in my hand that I am condemned to die, and after that to come to judgment, and I find that I am not willing to do the first, nor able to do the second.

Then said Evangelist, Why not willing to die, since this life is attended with so many evils? The man answered, Because I fear that this burden that is upon my back will sink me lower than the grave, and I shall fall into Tophet. And, sir, if I be not fit to go to prison, I am not fit to go to judgment, and from thence to execution; and the thoughts of these things make me cry.

Tophet. A ravine outside Jerusalem into which the city refuse was cast and burned. It came to signify a place of horror and terror.

Then said Evangelist, If this be thy condition, why standest thou still? He answered, Because I know not whither to go. Then he gave him a parchment roll, and there was written within, " Flee from the wrath to come."

The man therefore read it, and looking upon Evangelist very carefully, said, Whither must I fly? Then said Evangelist, pointing with his finger over a very wide field, Do you see yonder wicket-gate? The man said, No. Then said the other, Do you see yonder shining light? He said, I think I do. Then said Evangelist, Keep that light in your eye, and go up directly thereto: so shalt thou see the gate; at which when thou knockest it shall be told thee what thou shalt do. So I saw in my dream that the man began to run. Now, he had not run far from his own door, but his wife and children perceiving it, began to cry after him to return; but the man put his fingers in his ears, and ran on, crying, Life! life! eternal life! So he looked not behind him, but fled towards the middle of the plain.

OBSTINATE AND PLIABLE FOLLOW CHRISTIAN

The neighbours also came out to see him run; and as he ran, some mocked, others threatened, and some cried after him to return; and, among

those that did so, there were two that resolved to fetch him back by force. The name of the one was Obstinate, and the name of the other Pliable. Now by this time, the man was got a good distance from them; but, however, they were resolved to pursue him, which they did, and in a little time they overtook him. Then said the man, Neighbours, wherefore are ye come? They said, To persuade you to go back with us. But he said, That can by no means be; you dwell, said he, in the City of Destruction, the place also where I was born: I see it to be so; and dying there, sooner or later, you will sink lower than the grave, into a place that burns with fire and brimstone: be content, good neighbours, and go along with me.

Obst. What! said Obstinate, and leave our friends and our comforts behind us?

Chr. Yes, said Christian (for that was his name), because that ALL which you shall forsake is not worthy to be compared with a little of that which I am seeking to enjoy; and if you will go along with me, and hold it, you shall fare as I myself; for there, where I go, is enough and to spare. Come away, and prove my words.

Obst. What are the things you seek, since you leave all the world to find them?

Chr. I seek an inheritance incorruptible, undefiled, and that fadeth not away, and it is laid

up in heaven, and safe there, to be bestowed, at the time appointed, on them that diligently seek it. Read it so, if you will, in my book.

Obst. Tush! said Obstinate, away with your book. Will you go back with us or no?

Chr. No, not I, said the other, because I have laid my hand to the plough.

Obst. Come then, neighbour Pliable, let us turn again, and go home without him; there is a company of these crazy-headed coxcombs, that, when they take a fancy by the end, are wiser in their own eyes than seven men that can render a reason.

Pli. Then said Pliable, Don't revile; if what the good Christian says is true, the things he looks after are better than ours: my heart inclines to go with my neighbour.

Obst. What! more fools still! Be ruled by me, and go back; who knows whither such a brain-sick fellow will lead you? Go back, go back, and be wise.

Chr. Nay, but do thou come with thy neighbour, Pliable; there are such things to be had which I spoke of, and many more glories besides. If you believe not me, read here in this book; and for the truth of what is expressed therein, behold all is confirmed by the blood of Him that made it.

Pli. Well, neighbour Obstinate, said Pliable,

I begin to come to a point; I intend to go along with this good man, and to cast in my lot with him; but, my good companion, do you know the way to this desired place?

Chr. I am directed by a man, whose name is Evangelist, to speed me to a little gate that is before us, where we shall receive instructions about the way.

Pli. Come, then, good neighbour, let us be going. Then they went both together.

Obst. And I will go back to my place, said Obstinate; I will be no companion of such misled, fantastical fellows.

Now, I saw in my dream, that, when Obstinate was gone back, Christian and Pliable went talking over the plain; and thus they began their discourse:

Chr. Come, neighbour Pliable, how do you do? I am glad you are persuaded to go along with me. Had even Obstinate himself but felt what I have felt of the powers and terrors of what is yet unseen, he would not thus lightly have given us the back.

Pli. Come, neighbour Christian, since there are none but us two here, tell me now further what the things are, and how to be enjoyed, whither we are going.

Chr. I can better conceive of them with my mind, than speak of them with my tongue; but

yet, since you are desirous to know, I will read of them in my book.

Pli. And do you think that the words of your book are certainly true?

Chr. Yes, verily; for it was made by Him that cannot lie.

Pli. Well said; what things are they?

Chr. There is an endless kingdom to be inhabited, and everlasting life to be given us, that we may inhabit that kingdom for ever.

Pli. Well said; and what else?

Chr. There are crowns of glory to be given us, and garments that will make us shine like the sun in the firmament of heaven!

Pli. This is very pleasant; and what else?

Chr. There shall be no more crying, nor sorrow; for He that is owner of the place will wipe all tears from our eyes.

Pli. And what company shall we have there?

Chr. There we shall be with seraphim and cherubim, creatures that will dazzle your eyes to look on them. There also you shall meet with thousands and ten thousands that have gone before us to that place; none of them are hurtful, but loving and holy; every one walking in the sight of God, and standing in his presence with acceptance for ever. In a word, there we shall see the elders with their golden crowns; there we shall see the holy virgins with their

golden harps; there we shall see men that by the world were cut in pieces, burnt in flames, eaten of beasts, drowned in the seas, for the love that they bare to the Lord of the place, all well, and clothed with immortality as with a garment.

Pli. The hearing of this is enough to ravish one's heart. But are these things to be enjoyed? How shall we get to be sharers thereof?

Chr. The Lord, the Governor of the country, hath recorded that in this book; the substance of which is, If we be truly willing to have it, he will bestow it upon us freely.

Pli. Well, my good companion, glad am I to hear of these things; come on, let us mend our pace.

Chr. I cannot go so fast as I would, by reason of this burden that is on my back.

THE SLOUGH OF DESPOND

Now, I saw in my dream, that just as they had ended this talk they drew near to a very miry slough, that was in the midst of the plain; and they, being heedless, did both fall suddenly into the bog. The name of the slough was Despond. Here, therefore, they wallowed for a time, being grievously bedaubed with the dirt; and Christian, because of the burden that was on his back, began to sink in the mire.

Pli. Then said Pliable, Ah! neighbour Christian, where are you now?

Chr. Truly, said Christian, I do not know.

Pli. At this Pliable began to be offended, and angrily said to his fellow, Is this the happiness you have told me all this while of? If we have such ill speed at our first setting out, what may we expect betwixt this and our journey's end? May I get out again with my life, you shall possess the brave country alone for me. And, with that, he gave a desperate struggle or two, and got out of the mire on that side of the slough which was next to his own house: so away he went, and Christian saw him no more.

Wherefore Christian was left to tumble in the Slough of Despond alone: but still he endeavoured to struggle to that side of the slough that was still further from his own house, and next to the wicket-gate; the which he did, but could not get out, because of the burden that was upon his back: but I beheld in my dream, that a man came to him, whose name was Help, and asked him, What he did there?

Chr. Sir, said Christian, I was bid go this way by a man called Evangelist, who directed me also to yonder gate, that I might escape the wrath to come; and as I was going thither I fell in here.

Help. But why did not you look for the steps?

HELP RAISES CHRISTIAN
OUT OF THE SLOUGH OF DESPOND

Chr. Fear followed me so hard, that I fled the next way and fell in.

Help. Then said he, Give me thy hand: so he gave him his hand, and he drew him out, and set him upon sound ground, and bid him go on his way.

Then I stepped to him that plucked him out, and said, Sir, wherefore, since over this place is the way from the City of Destruction to yonder gate, is it that this plat is not mended, that poor travellers might go thither with more security? And he said unto me, This miry slough is such a place as cannot be mended; it is the descent whither the scum and filth that attends conviction for sin doth continually run, and therefore it is called the Slough of Despond; for still, as the sinner is awakened about his lost condition, there ariseth in his soul many fears, and doubts, and discouraging apprehensions, which all of them get together, and settle in this place. And this is the reason of the badness of this ground.

It is not the pleasure of the King that this place should remain so bad. His labourers also have, by the direction of His Majesty's surveyors, been for above sixteen hundred years employed about this patch of ground, if perhaps it might have been mended: yea, and to my knowledge,

Plat. A flat piece of ground (*cf.* plateau).

said he, here have been swallowed up at least twenty thousand cart-loads, yea, millions of wholesome instructions, that have at all seasons been brought from all places of the King's dominions, and they that can tell, say they are the best materials to make good ground of the place; if so be, it might have been mended, but it is the Slough of Despond still, and so will be when they have done what they can.

True, there are, by the direction of the Law-giver, certain good and substantial steps, placed even through the very midst of the slough; but at such time as this place doth much spew out its filth, as it doth against change of weather, these steps are hardly seen; or, if they be, men, through the dizziness of their heads, step beside, and then they are bemired to purpose, notwith-standing the steps be there; but the ground is good when they are once got in at the gate.

Now, I saw in my dream, that by this time Pliable was got home to his house again, so that his neighbours came to visit him; and some of them called him wise man for coming back, and some called him fool for hazarding himself with Christian: others, again, did mock at his coward-liness; saying, Surely, since you began to venture, I would not have been so base to have given out for a few difficulties. So Pliable sat sneaking among them. But at last he got more confidence,

and then they all turned their tales, and began
to deride poor Christian behind his back. And
thus much concerning Pliable.

CHRISTIAN MEETS MR. WORLDLY WISEMAN

Now, as Christian was walking solitarily by
himself, he espied one afar off, come crossing over
the field to meet him; and their hap was to meet
just as they were crossing the way of each other.
The gentleman's name that met him was Mr.
Worldly Wiseman: he dwelt in the town of
Carnal Policy, a very great town, and also hard-
by from whence Christian came. This man, then,
meeting with Christian, and having some inkling
of him,—for Christian's setting forth from the
City of Destruction was much noised abroad,
not only in the town where he dwelt, but also it
began to be the town talk in some other places,
—Mr. Worldly Wiseman, therefore, having some
guess of him, by beholding his laborious going,
by observing his sighs and groans, and the like,
began thus to enter into some talk with Christian.

World. How now, good fellow, whither away
after this burdened manner?

Mr. Worldly Wiseman is content with getting along
comfortably in this world. He and his fellow citizens care
only for worldly (carnal) things.

Chr. A burdened manner, indeed, as ever, I think, poor creature had! And whereas you ask me, Whither away? I tell you, Sir, I am going to yonder wicket-gate before me; for there, as I am informed, I shall be put into a way to be rid of my heavy burden.

World. Hast thou a wife and children?

Chr. Yes; but I am so laden with this burden, that I cannot take that pleasure in them as formerly; methinks I am as if I had none.

World. Wilt thou hearken unto me if I give thee counsel?

Chr. If it be good, I will; for I stand in need of good counsel.

World. I would advise thee, then, that thou with all speed get thyself rid of thy burden; for thou wilt never be settled in thy mind till then; nor canst thou enjoy the benefits of the blessing which God hath bestowed upon thee till then.

Chr. That is that which I seek, for ever to be rid of this heavy burden; but get it off myself, I cannot; nor is there any man in our country that can take it off my shoulders; therefore am I going this way, as I told you, that I may be rid of my burden.

World. Who bid thee go this way to be rid of thy burden?

Chr. A man that appeared to me to be a very

great and honourable person; his name, as I remember, is Evangelist.

World. I beshrew him for his counsel! there is not a more dangerous and troublesome way in the world than is that unto which he hath directed thee; and that thou shalt find, if thou wilt be ruled by his counsel. Thou hast met with something, as I perceive already; for I see the dirt of the Slough of Despond is upon thee; but that slough is the beginning of the sorrows that do attend those that go on in that way. Hear me, I am older than thou; thou art like to meet with, in the way which thou goest, wearisomeness, painfulness, hunger, perils, nakedness, sword, lions, dragons, darkness, and, in a word, death, and what not! These things are certainly true, having been confirmed by many testimonies. And why should a man so carelessly cast away himself, by giving heed to a stranger?

Chr. Why, Sir, this burden upon my back is more terrible to me than are all these things which you have mentioned; nay, methinks I care not what I meet with in the way, if so be I can also meet with deliverance from my burden.

World. How camest thou by the burden at first?

Chr. By reading this book in my hand.

World. I thought so; and it is happened unto thee as to other weak men, who, meddling with

things too high for them, do suddenly fall into thy distractions; which distractions do not only unman men, as thine, I perceive, have done thee, but they run them upon desperate ventures to obtain they know not what.

Chr. I know what I would obtain; it is ease for my heavy burden.

World. But why wilt thou seek for ease this way, seeing so many dangers attend it? especially since, hadst thou but patience to hear me, I could direct thee to the obtaining of what thou desirest, without the dangers that thou in this way wilt run thyself into; yea, and the remedy is at hand. Besides, I will add, that, instead of those dangers, thou shalt meet with much safety, friendship, and content.

Chr. Pray, Sir, open this secret to me.

World. Why, in yonder village — the village is named Morality — there dwells a gentleman whose name is Legality, a very judicious man, and a man of a very good name, that has skill to help men off with such burdens as thine are from their shoulders: yea, to my knowledge, he hath done a great deal of good this way; ay, and besides, he hath skill to cure those that are somewhat crazed in their wits with their burdens.

Mr. Legality and his son are eager to observe the letter of the Law. They are ignorant of the spirit and teaching of Christ.

To him, as I said, thou mayest go, and be helped presently. His house is not quite a mile from this place, and if he should not be at home himself, he hath a pretty young man to his son, whose name is Civility, that can do it (to speak on) as well as the old gentleman himself; there, I say, thou mayest be eased of thy burden; and if thou art not minded to go back to thy former habitation, as, indeed, I would not wish thee, thou mayest send for thy wife and children to thee to this village, where there are houses now standing empty, one of which thou mayest have at reasonable rates; provision is there also cheap and good; and that which will make thy life the more happy is, to be sure, there thou shalt live by honest neighbours, in credit and good fashion.

Now was Christian somewhat at a stand; but presently he concluded, If this be true, which this gentleman hath said, my wisest course is to take his advice; and with that he thus further spoke:

Chr. Sir, which is my way to this honest man's house?

World. Do you see yonder high hill?

Chr. Yes, very well.

World. By that hill you must go, and the first house you come at is his.

EVANGELIST REBUKES CHRISTIAN

So Christian turned out of his way to go to Mr. Legality's house for help; but, behold, when he was got now hard by the hill, it seemed so high, and also that side of it that was next the way-side did hang so much over, that Christian was afraid to venture further, lest the hill should fall on his head; wherefore there he stood still, and wotted not what to do. Also his burden now seemed heavier to him than while he was in his way. There came also flashes of fire out of the hill, that made Christian afraid that he should be burned. Here, therefore, he sweat and did quake for fear.

And now he began to be sorry that he had taken Mr. Worldly Wiseman's counsel. And with that he saw Evangelist coming to meet him; at the sight also of whom he began to blush for shame. So Evangelist drew nearer and nearer; and coming up to him he looked upon him with a severe and dreadful countenance, and thus began to reason with Christian:

Evan. What dost thou here, Christian? said he: at which words Christian knew not what to answer; wherefore at present he stood speechless before him. Then said Evangelist further, Art not thou the man that I found crying without the walls of the City of Destruction?

Chr. Yes, dear Sir, I am the man.

Evan. Did not I direct thee the way to the little wicket-gate?

Chr. Yes, dear Sir, said Christian.

Evan. How is it, then, that thou art so quickly turned aside? for thou art now out of the way.

Chr. I met with a gentleman so soon as I had got over the Slough of Despond, who persuaded me that I might, in the village before me, find a man that could take off my burden.

Evan. What was he?

Chr. He looked like a gentleman, and talked much to me, and got me at last to yield; so I came hither: but when I beheld this hill, and how it hangs over the way, I suddenly made a stand, lest it should fall on my head.

Evan. What said that gentleman to you?

Chr. Why, he asked me whither I was going? And I told him.

Evan. And what said he then?

Chr. He asked me if I had a family? And I told him. But, said I, I am so laden with the burden that is on my back, that I cannot take pleasure in them as formerly.

Evan. And what said he then?

Chr. He bid me with speed get rid of my burden; and I told him it was ease that I sought. And, said I, I am therefore going to yonder gate,

to receive further direction how I may get to the place of deliverance. So he said that he would show me a better way, and shorter, not so attended with difficulties as the way, Sir, that you set me in; which way, said he, will direct you to a gentleman's house that hath skill to take off these burdens; so I believed him, and turned out of that way into this, if haply I might be soon eased of my burden. But when I came to this place, and beheld things as they are, I stopped for fear (as I said) of danger: but I now know not what to do.

Evan. Then, said Evangelist, stand still a little, that I may show thee the words of God. So he stood trembling. Then said Evangelist, "See that ye refuse not him that speaketh." Thou hast begun to reject the counsel of the Most High, and to draw back thy foot from the way of peace, even almost to the hazarding of thy perdition.

Then Christian fell down at his feet as dead, crying, "Woe is me, for I am undone!" At the sight of which, Evangelist caught him by the right hand, saying, "All manner of sin and blasphemies shall be forgiven unto men." "Be not faithless, but believing." Then did Christian again a little revive, and stood up trembling, as at first, before Evangelist.

Then Evangelist proceeded, saying, Give more

earnest heed to the things that I shall tell thee of. I will now show thee who it was that deluded thee, and who it was also to whom he sent thee. The man that met thee is one Worldly Wiseman, and rightly is he so called; partly, because he savoureth only the doctrine of this world (therefore he always goes to the town of Morality to church): and partly, because he loveth that doctrine best, for it saveth him best from the cross. And because he is of this carnal temper, therefore he seeketh to prevent my ways, though right. Now there are three things in this man's counsel, that thou must utterly abhor.

1. His turning thee out of the way. 2. His labouring to render the cross odious to thee. And, 3. His setting thy feet in that way that leadeth unto the administration of death.

He to whom thou wast sent for ease, being by name Legality, is not able to set thee free from thy burden. No man was as yet ever rid of his burden by him; no, nor ever is like to be: ye cannot be justified by the works of the law; for by the deeds of the law no man living can be rid of his burden: therefore, Mr. Worldly Wiseman is an alien, and Mr. Legality is a cheat; and for his son Civility, notwithstanding his simpering looks, he is but a hypocrite and cannot help thee. Believe me, there is nothing in all this

Carnal. Having to do with this mortal life only.

B

noise, that thou hast heard of these sottish men,
but a design to beguile thee of thy salvation,
by turning thee from the way in which I had
set thee.

Now Christian looked for nothing but death,
and began to cry out lamentably; even cursing
the time in which he met with Mr. Worldly
Wiseman; still calling himself a thousand fools
for hearkening to his counsel: he also was greatly
ashamed to think that this gentleman's arguments, flowing only from the flesh, should have
the prevalency with him as to cause him to
forsake the right way. This done, he applied
himself again to Evangelist in words and sense
as follows:

Chr. Sir, what think you? Is there hope?
May I now go back and go up to the wicket-
gate? Shall I not be abandoned for this, and
sent back from thence ashamed? I am sorry I
have hearkened to this man's counsel. But
may my sin be forgiven?

Evan. Then said Evangelist to him, Thy sin
is very great, for by it thou hast committed two
evils: thou hast forsaken the way that is good,
to tread in forbidden paths; yet will the man
at the gate receive thee, for he has good-will for
men; only, said he, take heed that thou turn
not aside again, " lest thou perish from the way,
when his wrath is kindled but a little." Then did

Christian address himself to go back; and Evangelist, after he had kissed him, gave him one smile, and bid him God-speed.

CHRISTIAN MEETS WITH GOOD-WILL

So he went on with haste, neither spake he to any man by the way; nor, if any asked him, would he vouchsafe them an answer. He went like one that was all the while treading on forbidden ground, and could by no means think himself safe, till again he was got into the way which he left, to follow Mr. Worldly Wiseman's counsel. So, in process of time Christian got up to the gate. Now, over the gate there was written, " Knock, and it shall be opened unto you." He knocked, therefore, more than once or twice.

At last there came a grave person to the gate, named Good-will, who asked who was there? and whence he came? and what he would have?

Chr. Here is a poor burdened sinner. I come from the City of Destruction, but am going to Mount Zion, that I may be delivered from the wrath to come. I would, therefore, Sir, since I am informed that by this gate is the way thither, know if you are willing to let me in?

Good-will. I am willing with all my heart, said he; and with that he opened the gate.

So when Christian was stepping in, the other

gave him a pull. Then said Christian, What means that? The other told him, A little distance from this gate, there is erected a strong castle, of which Beelzebub is the captain; from thence, both he and they that are with him shoot arrows at those that come up to this gate, if haply they may die before they can enter in.

Then said Christian, I rejoice and tremble. So when he was got in, the man of the gate asked him who directed him thither?

Chr. Evangelist bid me come hither, and knock (as I did); and he said that you, Sir, would tell me what I must do.

Good-will. An open door is set before thee, and no man can shut it.

Chr. Now I begin to reap the benefits of my hazards.

Good-will. But how is it that you came alone?

Chr. Because none of my neighbours saw their danger, as I saw mine.

Good-will. Did any of them know of your coming?

Chr. Yes; my wife and children saw me at the first, and called after me to turn again; also, some of my neighbours stood crying and calling after me to return; but I put my fingers in my ears, and so came on my way.

Good-will. But did none of them follow you, to persuade you to go back?

Chr. Yes, both Obstinate and Pliable; but

when they saw that they could not prevail, Obstinate went railing back, but Pliable came with me a little way.

Good-will. But why did he not come through?

Chr. We, indeed, came both together, until we came at the Slough of Despond, into the which we also suddenly fell. And then was my neighbour, Pliable, discouraged, and would not adventure further. Wherefore, getting out again on that side next to his own house, he told me I should possess the brave country alone for him; so he went his way, and I came mine—he after Obstinate, and I to this gate.

Good-will. Then said Good-will, Alas, poor man! is the celestial glory of so small esteem with him, that he counteth it not worth running the hazards of a few difficulties to obtain it?

Chr. Truly, said Christian, I have said the truth of Pliable, and if I should also say all the truth of myself, it will appear there is no betterment betwixt him and myself. It is true, he went back to his own house, but I also turned aside to go in the way of death, being persuaded thereto by the carnal arguments of one Mr. Worldly Wiseman.

Good-will. Oh! did he light upon you? What! he would have had you a-sought for ease at the hands of Mr. Legality. They are, both of them, a very cheat. But did you take his counsel?

Chr. Yes, as far as I durst; I went to find out

Mr. Legality, until I thought that the mountain that stands by his house would have fallen upon my head; wherefore, there I was forced to stop.

Good-will. That mountain has been the death of many, and will be the death of many more; it is well you escaped being by it dashed in pieces.

Chr. Why, truly, I do not know what had become of me there, had not Evangelist happily met me again, as I was musing in the midst of my dumps; but it was God's mercy that he came to me again, for else I had never come hither. But now I am come, such a one as I am, more fit, indeed, for death, by that mountain, than thus to stand talking with my Lord; but, oh, what a favour is this to me, that yet I am admitted entrance here!

Good-will. We make no objections against any, notwithstanding all that they have done before they came hither. They are "in no wise cast out"; and therefore, good Christian, come a little way with me, and I will teach thee about the way thou must go. Look before thee; dost thou see this narrow way? THAT is the way thou must go; it was cast up by the patriarchs, prophets, Christ, and his apostles; and it is as straight as a rule can make it. This is the way thou must go.

Chr. But, said Christian, are there no turnings or windings, by which a stranger may lose his way?

Good-will. Yes, there are many ways and they are crooked and wide. But thus thou mayest distinguish the right from the wrong, the right only being straight and narrow.

Then I saw in my dream, that Christian asked him further if he could not help him off with his burden that was upon his back; for as yet he had not got rid thereof, nor could he by any means get it off without help.

He told him, As to thy burden, be content to bear it, until thou comest to the place of deliverance; for there it will fall from thy back of itself.

Then Christian began to gird up his loins, and to address himself to his journey. So the other told him, That by that he was gone some distance from the gate, he would come at the house of the Interpreter, at whose door he should knock, and he would show him excellent things. Then Christian took his leave of his friend, and he again bid him God-speed.

THE HOUSE OF THE INTERPRETER

Then he went on till he came to the house of the Interpreter, where he knocked over and over;

House of the Interpreter. Christian is now through the wicket-gate and on his direct journey. On this road are certain resting-places. The Interpreter's House is the first; there he learns more of the meaning of things, and is helped and encouraged to meet the dangers of his pilgrimage.

at last one came to the door, and asked who was there.

Chr. Sir, here is a traveller, who was bid by an acquaintance of the good-man of this house to call here for my profit; I would therefore speak with the master of the house. So he called for the master of the house, who, after a little time, came to Christian, and asked him what he would have.

Chr. Sir, said Christian, I am a man that am come from the City of Destruction, and am going to the Mount Zion; and I was told by the man that stands at the gate, at the head of this way, that if I called here, you would show me excellent things, such as would be a help to me in my journey.

Inter. Then said the Interpreter, Come in; I will show that which will be profitable to thee. So he commanded his man to light the candle, and bid Christian follow him: so he had him into a private room, and bid his man open a door; the which when he had done, Christian saw the picture of a very grave person hang up against the wall; and this was the fashion of it. It had eyes lifted up to heaven, the best of books in his hand, the law of truth was written upon his lips, the world was behind his back. It stood as if it pleaded with men, and a crown of gold did hang over his head.

Chr. Then said Christian, What meaneth this?

Inter. The man whose picture this is, is one of a thousand. And whereas thou seest him with his eyes lift up to heaven, the best of books in his hand, and the law of truth writ on his lips, it is to show thee that his work is to know and unfold dark things to sinners ; even as also thou seest him stand as if he pleaded with men; and whereas thou seest the world as cast behind him, and that a crown hangs over his head, that is to show thee that slighting and despising the things that are present, for the love that he hath to his Master's service, he is sure in the world that comes next to have glory for his reward. Now, said the Interpreter, I have showed thee this picture first, because the man whose picture this is, is the only man whom the Lord of the place whither thou art going, hath authorised to be thy guide in all difficult places thou mayest meet with in the way; wherefore, take good heed to what I have showed thee, and bear well in thy mind what thou hast seen, lest in thy journey thou meet with some that pretend to lead thee right, but their way goes down to death.

Then he took him by the hand, and led him into a very large parlour that was full of dust, because never swept; the which, after he had reviewed a little while, the Interpreter called for a man to sweep. Now when he began to sweep,

*B

the dust began so abundantly to fly about, that Christian had almost therewith been choked. Then said the Interpreter to a damsel that stood by, Bring hither the water, and sprinkle the room; the which, when she had done, it was swept and cleansed with pleasure.

Chr. Then said Christian, What means this?

Inter. The Interpreter answered, This parlour is the heart of a man that was never sanctified by the sweet grace of the gospel; the dust is his original sin, and inward corruptions, that have defiled the whole man. He that began to sweep at first, is the Law; but she that brought water, and did sprinkle it, is the Gospel. This is to show thee, that when the Gospel comes in the sweet and precious influences thereof to the heart, then, I say, even as thou sawest the damsel lay the dust by sprinkling the floor with water, so is sin vanquished and subdued, and the soul made clean through the faith of it, and consequently fit for the King of glory to inhabit.

I saw, moreover, in my dream, that the Interpreter took him by the hand, and had him into a little room, where sat two little children, each one in his chair. The name of the eldest was Passion, and the name of the other Patience. Passion seemed to be much discontented; but Patience was very quiet. Then Christian asked, What is the reason of the discontent of Passion?

The Interpreter answered, The Governor of them would have him stay for his best things till the beginning of the next year; but he will have all now: but Patience is willing to wait.

Then I saw that one came to Passion, and brought him a bag of treasure, and poured it down at his feet: the which he took up and rejoiced therein, and withal laughed Patience to scorn. But I beheld but a while, and he had lavished all away, and had nothing left him but rags.

Chr. Then said Christian to the Interpreter, Expound this matter more fully to me.

Inter. So he said, These two lads are figures: Passion, of the men of this world; and Patience, of the men of that which is to come; for, as here thou seest, Passion will have all now this year, that is to say, in this world; so are the men of this world: they must have all their good things now, they cannot stay till next year, that is, until the next world, for their portion of good. That proverb, " A bird in the hand is worth two in the bush," is of more authority with them than are all the Divine testimonies of the good of the world to come. But as thou sawest that he had quickly lavished all away, and had presently left him nothing but rags; so will it be with all such men at the end of this world.

Chr. Then said Christian, Now I see that

Patience has the best wisdom, and that upon many accounts. First, because he stays for the best things. Second, and also because he will have the glory of his, when the other has nothing but rags.

Inter. Nay, you may add another, to wit, the glory of the next world will never wear out; but these are suddenly gone. Therefore Passion had not so much reason to laugh at Patience, because he had his good things first, as Patience will have to laugh at Passion, because he had his best things last.

Chr. Then I perceive it is not best to covet things that are now, but to wait for things to come.

Inter. You say the truth: " For the things which are seen are temporal; but the things which are not seen are eternal."

Then I saw in my dream that the Interpreter took Christian by the hand, and led him into a place where was a fire burning against a wall, and one standing by it, always casting much water upon it, to quench it; yet did the fire burn higher and hotter.

Then said Christian, What means this?

The Interpreter answered, This fire is the work of grace that is wrought in the heart; he that casts water upon it, to extinguish and put it out, is the Devil; but in that thou seest the fire not-

withstanding burn higher and hotter, thou shalt also see the reason of that. So he had him about to the backside of the wall, where he saw a man with a vessel of oil in his hand, of the which he did also continually cast, but secretly, into the fire.

Then said Christian, What means this?

The Interpreter answered, This is Christ, who continually, with the oil of his grace, maintains the work already begun in the heart: by the means of which, notwithstanding what the devil can do, the souls of his people prove gracious still. And in that thou sawest that the man stood behind the wall to maintain the fire, that is to teach thee that it is hard for the tempted to see how this work of grace is maintained in the soul.

I saw also, that the Interpreter took him again by the hand, and led him into a pleasant place, where was built a stately palace, beautiful to behold; at the sight of which Christian was greatly delighted. He saw also, upon the top thereof, certain persons walking, who were clothed all in gold.

Then said Christian, May we go in thither?

Then the Interpreter took him, and led him up towards the door of the palace; and behold, at the door stood a great company of men, as desirous to go in, but durst not. There also sat a man at a little distance from the door, at a

table-side, with a book and his ink-horn before him, to take the name of him that should enter therein; he saw also, that in the doorway stood many men in armour to keep it, being resolved to do the men that would enter what hurt and mischief they could. Now was Christian somewhat in amaze. At last, when every man started back for fear of the armed men, Christian saw a man of a very stout countenance come up to the man that sat there to write, saying, "Set down my name, Sir": the which when he had done, he saw the man draw his sword, and put an helmet upon his head, and rush toward the door upon the armed men, who laid upon him with deadly force; but the man, not at all discouraged, fell to cutting and hacking most fiercely. So after he had received and given many wounds to those that attempted to keep him out, he cut his way through them all, and pressed forward into the palace, at which there was a pleasant voice heard from those that were within, even of those that walked upon the top of the palace, saying—

> Come in, come in;
> Eternal glory thou shalt win.

So he went in, and was clothed with such garments as they. Then Christian smiled and said, I think verily I know the meaning of this.

Now, said Christian, let me go hence.

Then said the Interpreter to Christian, Hast thou considered all these things?

Chr. Yes, and they put me in hope and fear.

Inter. Well, keep all things so in thy mind that they may be as a goad in thy sides, to prick thee forward in the way thou must go. Then Christian began to gird up his loins, and to address himself to his journey. Then said the Interpreter, The Comforter be always with thee, good Christian, to guide thee in the way that leads to the City. So Christian went on his way.

CHRISTIAN LOSES HIS BURDEN

Now I saw in my dream, that the highway up which Christian was to go, was fenced on either side with a wall, and that wall was called Salvation. Up this way, therefore, did burdened Christian run, but not without great difficulty, because of the load on his back.

He ran thus till he came at a place somewhat ascending, and upon that place stood a cross, and a little below, in the bottom, a sepulchre. So I saw in my dream, that just as Christian came up with the cross, his burden loosed from off his shoulders, and fell from off his back, and began to tumble, and so continued to do, till it came to the mouth of the sepulchre, where it fell in, and I saw it no more.

Then was Christian glad and lightsome, and said, with a merry heart, "He hath given me rest by his sorrow, and life by his death." Then he stood still awhile to look and wonder; for it was very surprising to him, that the sight of the cross should thus ease him of his burden. He looked, therefore, and looked again, even till the springs that were in his head sent the waters down his cheeks. Now, as he stood looking and weeping, behold, three Shining Ones came to him and saluted him with "Peace be to thee." So the first said to him, "Thy sins be forgiven thee"; the second stripped him of his rags, and clothed him "with change of raiment"; the third also set a mark on his forehead, and gave him a roll with a seal upon it, which he bade him look on as he ran, and that he should give it in at the Celestial Gate. So they went their way.

Then Christian gave three leaps for joy, and went on singing.

SLOTH AND PRESUMPTION

I saw then in my dream, that he went on thus, even until he came at a bottom, where he saw, a little out of the way, three men fast asleep, with fetters upon their heels. The name of the

Bottom. A small valley; a dip in the road.

one was Simple, another Sloth, and the third Presumption.

Christian then seeing them lie in this case, went to them, if peradventure he might awake them, and cried, You are like them that sleep on the top of a mast, for the Dead Sea is under you—a gulf that hath no bottom. Awake, therefore, and come away; be willing also, and I will help you off with your irons. He also told them, If he that "goeth about like a roaring lion" comes by, you will certainly become a prey to his teeth. With that they looked upon him, and began to reply in this sort: Simple said, "I see no danger"; Sloth said, "Yet a little more sleep"; and Presumption said, "Every fat must stand upon its own bottom; what is the answer else that I should give thee?" And so they lay down to sleep again, and Christian went on his way.

FORMALIST AND HYPOCRISY

Yet was he troubled to think that men in that danger should so little esteem the kindness of him that so freely offered to help them, both by awakening of them, counselling of them, and proffering to help them off with their irons. And as he was troubled thereabout, he espied two

Fat, or *vat*. A vessel, or jar.

men come tumbling over the wall, on the left hand of the narrow way; and they made up apace to him. The name of the one was Formalist, and the name of the other Hypocrisy. So, as I said, they drew up unto him, who thus entered with them into discourse:

Chr. Gentlemen, whence came you, and whither go you?

Form. and *Hyp.* We were born in the land of Vain-glory, and are going for praise to Mount Sion.

Chr. Why came you not in at the gate which standeth at the beginning of the way? Know you not that it is written, that he that cometh not in by the door, " but climbeth up some other way, the same is a thief and a robber "?

Form. and *Hyp.* They said, That to go to the gate for entrance was, by all their countrymen, counted too far about; and that, therefore, their usual way was to make a short cut of it, and to climb over the wall, as they had done.

Chr. But will it not be counted a trespass against the Lord of the city whither we are bound, thus to violate his revealed will?

Form. and *Hyp.* They told him, That, as for that, he needed not to trouble his head thereabout; for what they did they had custom for;

Formalist. One who is zealous about the outward forms of religion, but careless of its real spirit.

and could produce, if need were, testimony that would witness it for more than a thousand years.

Chr. But, said Christian, will your practice stand a trial at law?

Form. and *Hyp*. They told him, That custom, it being of so long a standing as above a thousand years, would, doubtless, now be admitted as a thing legal by any impartial judge; and beside, said they, if we get into the way, what's matter which way we get in? if we are in, we are in; thou art but in the way, who, as we perceive, came in at the gate; and we are also in the way, that came tumbling over the wall; wherein, now, is thy condition better than ours?

Chr. I walk by the rule of my Master; you walk by the rude working of your fancies. You are counted thieves already, by the Lord of the way; therefore, I doubt you will not be found true men at the end of the way. You come in by yourselves, without his direction, and shall go out by yourselves, without his mercy.

To this they made him but little answer; only they bid him look to himself. Then I saw that they went on every man in his way, without much conference one with another; save that these two men told Christian, That as to laws and ordinances, they doubted not but they should as conscientiously do them as he; there-

Rude. Untaught; untrained.

fore, said they, we see not wherein thou differest from us but by the coat that is on thy back, which was, as we trow, given thee by some of thy neighbours, to hide the shame of thy nakedness.

Chr. By laws and ordinances you will not be saved, since you came not in by the door. And as for this coat that is on my back, it was given me by the Lord of the place whither I go; and that, as you say, to cover my nakedness with. And I take it as a token of his kindness to me; for I had nothing but rags before. And besides, thus I comfort myself as I go: Surely, think I, when I come to the gate of the city, the Lord thereof will know me for good, since I have his coat on my back—a coat that he gave me freely in the day that he stripped me of my rags. I have, moreover, a mark in my forehead, of which, perhaps, you have taken no notice, which one of my Lord's most intimate associates fixed there in the day that my burden fell off my shoulders. I will tell you, moreover, that I had then given me a roll, sealed, to comfort me by reading as I go on the way; I was also bid to give it in at the Celestial Gate, in token of my certain going in after it; all which things, I doubt, you want, and want them because you came not in at the gate.

To these things they gave him no answer;

only they looked upon each other, and laughed. Then I saw that they went on all, save that Christian kept before, who had no more talk but with himself, and that sometimes sighingly, and sometimes comfortably; also he would be often reading in the roll that one of the Shining Ones gave him, by which he was refreshed.

THE HILL DIFFICULTY

I beheld, then, that they all went on till they came to the foot of the Hill Difficulty; at the bottom of which was a spring. There were also in the same place two other ways besides that which came straight from the gate; one turned to the left hand, and the other to the right, at the bottom of the hill; but the narrow way lay right up the hill, and the name of the going up the side of the hill is called Difficulty. Christian now went to the spring, and drank thereof, to refresh himself, and then began to go up the hill.

The other two also came to the foot of the hill; but when they saw that the hill was steep and high, and that there were two other ways to go; and supposing also that these two ways might meet again, with that up which Christian went, on the other side of the hill; therefore they were resolved to go in those ways. Now the name of one of those ways was Danger, and

the name of the other Destruction. So the one took the way which is called Danger, which led him into a great wood, and the other took directly up the way to Destruction, which led him into a wide field, full of dark mountains, where he stumbled and fell, and rose no more.

I looked, then, after Christian, to see him go up the hill, where I perceived he fell from running to going, and from going to clambering upon his hands and his knees, because of the steepness of the place. Now, about the midway to the top of the hill was a pleasant arbour, made by the Lord of the hill for the refreshing of weary travellers; thither, therefore, Christian got, where also he sat down to rest him. Then he pulled his roll out of his bosom, and read therein to his comfort; he also now began afresh to take a review of the coat or garment that was given him as he stood by the cross. Thus pleasing himself awhile, he at last fell into a slumber, and thence into a fast sleep, which detained him in that place until it was almost night; and in his sleep his roll fell out of his hand. Now, as he was sleeping, there came one to him, and awaked him, saying, "Go to the ant, thou sluggard; consider her ways, and be wise." And with that Christian started up, and sped him on his way, and went apace, till he came to the top of the hill.

CHRISTIAN CLIMBS THE HILL DIFFICULTY

Now, when he was got up to the top of the hill, there came two men running to meet him amain; the name of the one was Timorous, and of the other, Mistrust; to whom Christian said, Sirs, what's the matter? You run the wrong way. Timorous answered, That they were going to the City of Zion, and had got up that difficult place; but, said he, the further we go, the more danger we meet with; wherefore we turned, and are going back again.

Yes, said Mistrust, for just before us lie a couple of lions in the way, whether sleeping or waking we know not, and we could not think, if we came within reach, but they would presently pull us in pieces.

Chr. Then said Christian, You make me afraid, but whither shall I fly to be safe? If I go back to mine own country, *that* is prepared for fire and brimstone, and I shall certainly perish there. If I can get to the Celestial City, I am sure to be in safety there. I must venture. To go back is nothing but death; to go forward is fear of death, and life everlasting beyond it. I will yet go forward. So Mistrust and Timorous ran down the hill, and Christian went on his way. But, thinking again of what he had heard from the men, he felt in his bosom for his roll, that he might read therein, and be comforted; but he felt, and found it not. Then was Christian

in great distress, and knew not what to do; for he wanted that which used to relieve him, and that which should have been his pass into the Celestial City. Here, therefore, he began to be much perplexed, and knew not what to do. At last he bethought himself that he had slept in the arbour that is on the side of the hill; and, falling down upon his knees, he asked God's forgiveness for that his foolish act, and then went back to look for his roll. But all the way he went back, who can sufficiently set forth the sorrow of Christian's heart! Sometimes he sighed, sometimes he wept, and oftentimes he chid himself for being so foolish to fall asleep in that place, which was erected only for a little refreshment for his weariness. Thus, therefore, he went back, carefully looking on this side and on that, all the way as he went, if happily he might find his roll, that had been his comfort so many times in his journey. He went thus, till he came again within sight of the arbour where he sat and slept; but that sight renewed his sorrow the more, by bringing again, even afresh, his evil of sleeping into his mind. Thus, therefore, he now went on bewailing his sinful sleep, saying, "O wretched man that I am!" that I should sleep in the day-time! that I should sleep in the midst of difficulty! that I should so indulge the flesh, as to use that rest for ease to my flesh,

which the Lord of the hill hath erected only for the relief of the spirits of pilgrims!

How many steps have I took in vain! Thus it happened to Israel, for their sin; they were sent back again by the way of the Red Sea; and I am made to tread those steps with sorrow, which I might have trod with delight, had it not been for this sinful sleep. How far might I have been on my way by this time! I am made to tread those steps thrice over, which I needed not to have trod but once; yea, now also I am like to be benighted, for the day is almost spent. Oh, that I had not slept!

Now, by this time he was come to the arbour again, where for a while he sat down and wept; but at last, as Christian would have it, looking sorrowfully down under the settle, there he espied his roll; the which he, with trembling and haste, catched up, and put it into his bosom. But who can tell how joyful this man was when he had gotten his roll again! for this roll was the assurance of his life and acceptance at the desired haven. Therefore he laid it up in his bosom, gave thanks to God for directing his eye to the place where it lay, and with joy and tears betook himself again to his journey. But oh, how nimbly now did he go up the rest of the hill! Yet, before he got up, the sun went down upon Christian; and this made him again recall the vanity of his

sleeping to his remembrance; and thus he again began to condole with himself: O thou sinful sleep: how, for thy sake, am I like to be benighted in my journey! I must walk without the sun; darkness must cover the path of my feet; and I must hear the noise of the doleful creatures, because of my sinful sleep. Now also he remembered the story that Mistrust and Timorous told him of, how they were frighted with the sight of the lions. Then said Christian to himself again, These beasts range in the night for their prey; and if they should meet with me in the dark, how should I shift them? How should I escape being by them torn in pieces? Thus he went on his way. But while he was thus bewailing his unhappy miscarriage, he lift up his eyes, and behold there was a very stately palace before him, the name of which was Beautiful; and it stood just by the highway side.

THE LIONS IN THE PATH

So I saw in my dream that he made haste and went forward, that if possible he might get lodging there. Now, before he had gone far, he entered into a very narrow passage, which was about a furlong off of the porter's lodge; and looking very narrowly before him as he went, he espied two lions in the way. Now, thought he,

I see the dangers that Mistrust and Timorous were driven back by. (The lions were chained, but he saw not the chains.) Then he was afraid, and thought also himself to go back after them, for he thought nothing but death was before him. But the porter at the lodge, whose name is Watchful, perceiving that Christian made a halt as if he would go back, cried unto him, saying, Is thy strength so small? Fear not the lions, for they are chained, and are placed there for trial of faith where it is, and for discovery of those that had none. Keep in the midst of the path, and no hurt shall come unto thee.

Then I saw that he went on, trembling for fear of the lions, but taking good heed to the directions of the porter; he heard them roar, but they did him no harm. Then he clapped his hands, and went on till he came and stood before the gate where the porter was.

THE PALACE BEAUTIFUL

Then said Christian to the porter, Sir, what house is this? And may I lodge here to-night? The porter answered, This house was built by the Lord of the hill, and he built it for the relief and security of pilgrims. The porter also asked whence he was, and whither he was going.

Chr. I am come from the City of Destruction,

and am going to Mount Zion; but because the sun is now set, I desire, if I may, to lodge here to-night.

Por. What is your name?

Chr. My name is now Christian, but my name at the first was Graceless.

Por. But how doth it happen that you come so late? The sun is set.

Chr. I had been here sooner, but that, " wretched man that I am! " I slept in the arbour that stands on the hill-side; nay I had, notwithstanding that, been here much sooner, but that, in my sleep, I lost my evidence, and came without it to the brow of the hill; and then feeling for it, and finding it not, I was forced, with sorrow of heart, to go back to the place where I slept my sleep, where I found it, and now I am come.

Por. Well, I will call out one of the virgins of this place, who will, if she likes your talk, bring you in to the rest of the family, according to the rules of the house. So Watchful, the porter, rang a bell, at the sound of which came out at the door of the house a grave and beautiful damsel, named Discretion, and asked why she was called.

The porter answered, This man is in a journey from the City of Destruction to Mount Zion, but being weary and benighted, he asked me if he

CHRISTIAN PASSES THE LIONS THAT GUARD
THE PALACE BEAUTIFUL

CHRISTIAN FACES THE LIONS. THAT OPENS

THE PALACE BEAUTIFUL.

might lodge here to-night; so I told him I would call for thee, who, after discourse had with him, mayest do as seemeth thee good, even according to the law of the house.

Then she asked him whence he was, and whither he was going; and he told her. She asked him also how he got into the way; and he told her. Then she asked him what he had seen and met with in the way; and he told her. And last she asked his name; so he said, It is Christian, and I have so much the more a desire to lodge here to-night, because, by what I perceive, this place was built by the Lord of the hill, for the relief and security of pilgrims. So she smiled, but the water stood in her eyes; and after a little pause, she said, I will call forth two or three more of the family. So she ran to the door, and called out Prudence, Piety, and Charity, who, after a little more discourse with him, had him into the family; and many of them, meeting him at the threshold of the house, said, " Come in, thou blessed of the Lord "; this house was built by the Lord of the hill, on purpose to enter-tain such pilgrims in. Then he bowed his head, and followed them into the house. So when he was come in and sat down, they gave him some-thing to drink, and consented together, that until supper was ready, some of them should have some particular discourse with Christian,

c

for the best improvement of time; and they appointed Piety, and Prudence, and Charity to discourse with him; and thus they began:

Piety. Come, good Christian, since we have been so loving to you, to receive you in our house this night, let us, if perhaps we may better ourselves thereby, talk with you of all things that have happened to you in your pilgrimage.

Chr. With a very good will, and I am glad that you are so well disposed.

Piety. What moved you at first to betake yourself to a pilgrim's life?

Chr. I was driven out of my native country, by a dreadful sound that was in mine ears: to wit, that unavoidable destruction did attend me, if I abode in that place where I was.

Piety. But how did it happen that you came out of your country this way?

Chr. It was as God would have it; for when I was under the fears of destruction, I did not know whither to go; but by chance there came a man, even to me, as I was trembling and weeping, whose name is Evangelist, and he directed me to the wicket-gate, which else I should never have found, and so set me into the way that hath led me directly to this house.

Piety. But did you not come by the house of the Interpreter?

Chr. Yes, and did see such things there, the

remembrance of which will stick by me as long as I live.

Piety. Was that all that you saw at the house of the Interpreter?

Chr. No; he took me and had me where he showed me a stately palace, and how the people were clad in gold that were in it; and how there came a venturous man and cut his way through the armed men that stood in the door to keep him out, and how he was bid to come in, and win eternal glory. Methought those things did ravish my heart! I would have stayed at that good man's house a twelvemonth, but that I knew I had further to go.

Piety. And what saw you else in the way?

Chr. Saw! why, I went but a little further, and I saw one, as I thought in my mind, hang bleeding upon the tree; and the very sight of him made my burden fall off my back (for I groaned under a very heavy burden), but then it fell down from off me. It was a strange thing to me, for I never saw such a thing before; yea, and while I stood looking up, for then I could not forbear looking, three Shining Ones came to me. One of them testified that my sins were forgiven me; another stripped me of my rags, and gave me this broidered coat which you see; and the third set the mark which you see in my forehead, and gave me this sealed

roll. (And with that he plucked it out of his bosom.)

Piety. But you saw more than this, did you not?

Chr. The things that I have told you were the best; yet some other matters I saw, as, namely: I saw three men, Simple, Sloth, and Presumption, lie asleep a little out of the way, as I came, with irons upon their heels; but do you think I could awake them? I also saw Formality and Hypocrisy come tumbling over the wall, to go, as they pretended, to Zion, but they were quickly lost, even as I myself did tell them; but they would not believe. But above all, I found it hard work to get up this hill, and as hard to come by the lions' mouths; and truly if it had not been for the good man, the porter that stands at the gate, I do not know but that after all I might have gone back again; but now, I thank God I am here, and I thank you for receiving of me.

Then Prudence thought good to ask him a few questions, and desired his answer to them.

Prud. Do you not think sometimes of the country from whence you came?

Chr. Yes, but with much shame and detestation: "truly, if I had been mindful of that country from whence I came out, I might have had opportunity to have returned; but now I desire a better country, that is, an heavenly."

Prud. Do you not yet bear away with you some of the things that then you were conversant withal?

Chr. Yes, but greatly against my will; especially my inward and carnal cogitations, with which all my countrymen, as well as myself, were delighted; but now all those things are my grief; and might I but choose mine own things, I would choose never to think of those things more; but when I would be doing of that which is best, that which is worst is with me.

Prud. Do you not find sometimes, as if those things were vanquished, which at other times are your perplexity?

Chr. Yes, but that is seldom; but they are to me golden hours in which such things happen to me.

Prud. Can you remember by what means you find your annoyances, at times, as if they were vanquished?

Chr. Yes, when I think what I saw at the cross, that will do it; and when I look upon my broidered coat, that will do it; also when I look into the roll that I carry in my bosom, that will do it; and when my thoughts wax warm about whither I am going, that will do it.

Prud. And what is it that makes you so desirous to go to Mount Zion?

Chr. Why, there I hope to see him alive that

did hang dead on the cross; and there I hope
to be rid of all those things that to this day are
in me an annoyance to me; there, they say, there
is no death; and there I shall dwell with such
company as I like best. For, to tell you truth,
I love him, because I was by him eased of my
burden; and I am weary of my inward sickness.
I would fain be where I shall die no more, and
with the company that shall continually cry,
" Holy, Holy, Holy! "

Then said Charity to Christian, Have you a
family? Are you a married man?

Chr. I have a wife and four small children.

Char. And why did you not bring them along
with you?

Chr. Then Christian wept, and said, Oh, how
willingly would I have done it! but they were
all of them utterly averse to my going on
pilgrimage.

Char. But you should have talked to them,
and have endeavoured to have shown them the
danger of being behind.

Chr. So I did; and told them also what God
had shown to me of the destruction of our city;
" but I seemed to them as one that mocked,"
and they believed me not.

Char. And did you pray to God that he would
bless your counsel to them?

Chr. Yes, and that with much affection: for

you must think that my wife and poor children were very dear unto me.

Char. But did you tell them of your own sorrow, and fear of destruction? for I suppose that destruction was visible enough to you.

Chr. Yes, over, and over, and over. They might also see my fears in my countenance, in my tears, and also in my trembling under the apprehension of the judgment that did hang over our heads; but all was not sufficient to prevail with them to come with me.

Char. But what could they say for themselves, why they came not?

Chr. Why, my wife was afraid of losing this world, and my children were given to the foolish delights of youth: so what by one thing, and what by another, they left me to wander in this manner alone.

Char. But did you not, with your vain life, damp all that you by words used by way of persuasion to bring them away with you?

Chr. Indeed, I cannot commend my life; for I am conscious to myself of many failings therein: I know also, that a man by his conversation may soon overthrow what by argument or persuasion he doth labour to fasten upon others for their good. Yet this I can say, I was very wary of

Conversation. General way of life: only later was it limited to talking.

giving them occasion, by any unseemly action, to make them averse to going on pilgrimage. Yea, for this very thing they would tell me I was too precise, and that I denied myself of things, for their sakes, in which they saw no evil. Nay, I think I may say, that if what they saw in me did hinder them, it was my great tenderness in sinning against God, or of doing any wrong to my neighbour.

Now I saw in my dream, that thus they sat talking together until supper was ready. So when they had made ready, they sat down to meat. Now the table was furnished "with fat things, and with wine that was well refined": and all their talk at the table was about the Lord of the hill; as, namely, about what he had done, and wherefore he did what he did, and why he had built that house. And by what they said, I perceived that he had been a great warrior, and had fought with and slain "him that had the power of death," but not without great danger to himself, which made me love him the more.

For, as they said, and as I believe (said Christian), he did it with the loss of much blood; but that which put glory of grace into all he did, was, that he did it out of pure love to his country. And besides, there were some of them of the household that said they had been and spoke with him since he did die on the cross; and

they have attested that they had it from his own lips, that he is such a lover of poor pilgrims, that the like is not to be found from the east to the west.

They, moreover, gave an instance of what they affirmed, and that was, he had stripped himself of his glory, that he might do this for the poor; and that they heard him say and affirm, " that he would not dwell in the mountain of Zion alone." They said, moreover, that he had made many pilgrims princes, though by nature they were beggars born, and their original had been the dunghill.

Thus they discoursed together till late at night; and after they had committed themselves to their Lord for protection, they betook themselves to rest: the Pilgrim they laid in a large upper chamber, whose window opened toward the sun-rising: the name of the chamber was Peace, where he slept till break of day, and then he awoke.

CHRISTIAN IS ARMED

So in the morning they all got up; and, after some more discourse, they told him that he should not depart till they had shown him the rarities of that place. And first they had him into the study, where they showed him records of the greatest antiquity; in which, as I remember

*c

in my dream, they showed him first the pedi-
gree of the Lord of the hill, that he was the
son of the Ancient of Days, and came by that
eternal generation. Here also was more fully
recorded the acts that he had done, and the
names of many hundreds that he had taken into
his service; and how he had placed them in such
habitations, that could neither by length of days,
nor decays of nature, be dissolved.

Then they read to him some of the worthy acts
that some of his servants had done: as, how they
had "subdued kingdoms, wrought righteousness,
obtained promises, stopped the mouths of lions,
quenched the violence of fire, escaped the edge
of the sword, out of weakness were made strong,
waxed valiant in fight, and turned to flight the
armies of the aliens."

They then read again, in another part of the
records of the house, where it was showed how
willing their Lord was to receive into his favour
any, even any, though they in time past had
offered great affronts to his person and pro-
ceedings. Here also were several other histories
of many other famous things, of all which Christian had a view; as of things both ancient
and modern; together with prophecies and pre-
dictions of things that have their certain accom-
plishment, both to the dread and amazement of
enemies, and the comfort and solace of pilgrims,

The next day they took him and had him into the armoury, where they showed him all manner of furniture, which their Lord had provided for pilgrims, as sword, shield, helmet, breastplate, *all-prayer*, and shoes that would not wear out. And there was here enough of this to harness out as many men for the service of their Lord as there be stars in heaven for multitude.

They also showed him some of the engines with which some of his servants had done wonderful things. They showed him Moses' rod; the hammer and nail with which Jael slew Sisera; the pitchers, trumpets, and lamps too, with which Gideon put to flight the armies of Midian. Then they showed him the ox's goad wherewith Shamgar slew six hundred men. They showed him also the jaw-bone with which Samson did such mighty feats. They showed him, moreover, the sling and stone with which David slew Goliath of Gath; and the sword, also, with which their Lord will kill the Man of Sin, in the day that he shall rise up to the prey. They showed him, besides, many excellent things, with which Christian was much delighted. This done, they went to their rest again.

Then I saw in my dream, that on the morrow

Engines. Implements; weapons.
Shamgar. One of the judges of Israel. He slew a great host of the Philistines with an ox-goad.

he got up to go forward; but they desired him to stay till the next day also; and then, said they, we will, if the day be clear, show you the Delectable Mountains, which, they said, would yet further add to his comfort, because they were nearer the desired haven than the place where at present he was; so he consented and stayed. When the morning was up, they had him to the top of the house, and bade him look south; so he did: and behold, at a great distance, he saw a most pleasant mountainous country, beautified with woods, vineyards, fruits of all sorts, flowers also, with springs and fountains, very delectable to behold. Then he asked the name of the country. They said it was Immanuel's Land; and it is as common, said they, as this hill is, to and for all the pilgrims. And when thou comest there from hence, said they, thou mayest see to the gate of the Celestial City, as the shepherds that live there will make appear.

Now he bethought himself of setting forward, and they were willing he should. But first, said they, let us go again into the armoury. So they did; and when they came there, they harnessed him from head to foot with what was of proof, lest, perhaps, he should meet with assaults in the way. He being, therefore, thus accoutred, walketh out with his friends to the gate, and

there he asked the porter if he saw any pilgrims pass by. Then the porter answered, Yes.

Chr. Pray, did you know him? said he.

Por. I asked him his name, and he told me it was Faithful.

Chr. Oh, said Christian, I know him; he is my townsman, my near neighbour; he comes from the place where I was born. How far do you think he may be before?

Por. He is got by this time below the hill.

Chr. Well, said Christian, good Porter, the Lord be with thee, and add to all thy blessings much increase, for the kindness that thou hast showed to me.

Then he began to go forward; but Discretion, Piety, Charity, and Prudence would accompany him down to the foot of the hill. So they went on together, reiterating their former discourses, till they came to go down the hill. Then said Christian, As it was difficult coming up, so, so far as I can see, it is dangerous going down. Yes, said Prudence, so it is, for it is a hard matter for a man to go down into the Valley of Humiliation, as thou art now, and to catch no slip by the way; therefore, said they, are we come out to accompany thee down the hill. So he began to go down, but very warily; yet he caught a slip or two.

Then I saw in my dream that these good

companions, when Christian was gone to the bottom of the hill, gave him a loaf of bread, a bottle of wine, and a cluster of raisins; and then he went on his way.

THE VALLEY OF HUMILIATION AND THE FIGHT WITH APOLLYON

But now, in this Valley of Humiliation, poor Christian was hard put to it; for he had gone but a little way, before he espied a foul fiend coming over the field to meet him; his name is Apollyon. Then did Christian begin to be afraid, and to cast in his mind whether to go back or to stand his ground. But he considered again that he had no armour for his back; and therefore thought that to turn the back to him might give him the greater advantage with ease to pierce him with his darts. Therefore he resolved to venture and stand his ground; for, thought he, had I no more in mine eye than the saving of my life, it would be the best way to stand.

So he went on, and Apollyon met him. Now the monster was hideous to behold; he was clothed with scales, like a fish (and they are his pride), he had wings like a dragon, feet like a bear, and out of his belly came fire and smoke, and his mouth was as the mouth of a lion. When he was come up to Christian, he beheld him with

a disdainful countenance, and thus began to question with him:

Apol. Whence come you? and whither are you bound?

Chr. I am come from the City of Destruction, which is the place of all evil, and am going to the City of Zion.

Apol. By this I perceive thou art one of my subjects, for all that country is mine, and I am the prince and god of it. How is it, then, that thou hast run away from thy king? Were it not that I hope thou mayest do me more service, I would strike thee now, at one blow, to the ground.

Chr. I was born, indeed, in your dominions, but your service was hard, and your wages such as a man could not live on, " for the wages of sin is death "; therefore, when I was come to years, I did as other considerate persons do, look out, if, perhaps, I might mend myself.

Apol. There is no prince that will thus lightly lose his subjects, neither will I as yet lose thee; but since thou complainest of my service and wages, be content to go back: what our country will afford, I do here promise to give thee.

Chr. But I have let myself to another, even to the King of princes; and how can I, with fairness, go back with thee?

Apol. Thou hast done in this, according to the proverb, " Changed a bad for a worse ";

but it is ordinary for those that have professed themselves his servants, after a while to give him the slip, and return again to me. Do thou so too, and all shall be well.

Chr. I have given him my faith, and sworn my allegiance to him; how, then, can I go back from this, and not be hanged as a traitor?

Apol. Thou didst the same to me, and yet I am willing to pass by all, if now thou wilt yet turn again and go back.

Chr. What I promised thee was in my nonage; and, besides, I count the Prince under whose banner now I stand is able to absolve me; yea, and to pardon also what I did as to my compliance with thee; and besides, O thou destroying Apollyon! to speak truth, I like his service, his wages, his servants, his government, his company and country, better than thine; and, therefore, leave off to persuade me further; I am his servant, and I will follow him.

Apol. Consider, again, when thou art in cool blood, what thou art like to meet with in the way that thou goest. Thou knowest that, for the most part, his servants come to an ill end, because they are transgressors against me and my ways. How many of them have been put to shameful deaths; and, besides, thou countest his service better than mine, whereas he never came yet

Nonage. Minority (before I was of age and responsible).

from the place where he is to deliver any that
served him out of their hands; but as for me,
how many times, as all the world very well
knows, have I delivered, either by power, or
fraud, those that have faithfully served me, from
him and his, though taken by them; and so I
will deliver thee.

Chr. His forbearing at present to deliver them
is on purpose to try their love, whether they
will cleave to him to the end; and as for the ill
end thou sayest they come to, that is most
glorious in their account; for, for present deliverance, they do not much expect it, for they
stay for their glory, and then they shall have it,
when their Prince comes in his and the glory of
the angels.

Apol. Thou hast already been unfaithful in
thy service to him; and how dost thou think
to receive wages of him?

Chr. Wherein, O Apollyon! have I been unfaithful to him?

Apol. Thou didst faint at first setting out,
when thou wast almost choked in the Gulf of
Despond; thou didst attempt wrong ways to be
rid of thy burden, whereas thou shouldest have
stayed till thy Prince had taken it off; thou
didst sinfully sleep and lose thy choice thing;
thou wast, also, almost persuaded to go back,
at the sight of the lions; and when thou talkest

of thy journey, and of what thou hast heard and seen, thou art inwardly desirous of vainglory in all that thou sayest or doest.

Chr. All this is true, and much more which thou hast left out; but the Prince whom I serve and honour is merciful, and ready to forgive; but, besides, these infirmities possessed me in thy country, for there I sucked them in; and I have groaned under them, been sorry for them, and have obtained pardon of my Prince.

Apol. Then Apollyon broke out into a grievous rage, saying, I am an enemy to this Prince; I hate his person, his laws, and people; I am come out on purpose to withstand thee.

Chr. Apollyon, beware what you do; for I am in the king's highway, the way of holiness; therefore take heed to yourself.

Apol. Then Apollyon straddled quite over the whole breadth of the way, and said, I am void of fear in this matter: prepare thyself to die; for I swear by my infernal den, that thou shalt go no further; here will I spill thy soul.

And with that he threw a flaming dart at his breast; but Christian had a shield in his hand, with which he caught it, and so prevented the danger of that.

Then did Christian draw, for he saw it was time to bestir him: and Apollyon as fast made at him, throwing darts as thick as hail; by the

THE FIGHT OF CHRISTIAN WITH APOLLYON

which, notwithstanding all that Christian could
do to avoid it, Apollyon wounded him in his
head, his hand, and foot. This made Christian
give a little back; Apollyon, therefore, followed
his work amain, and Christian again took courage,
and resisted as manfully as he could. This sore
combat lasted for above half a day, even till
Christian was almost quite spent; for you must
know that Christian, by reason of his wounds,
must needs grow weaker and weaker.

Then Apollyon, espying his opportunity, began
to gather up close to Christian, and wrestling
with him, gave him a dreadful fall; and with
that Christian's sword flew out of his hand. Then
said Apollyon, I am sure of thee now. And with
that he had almost pressed him to death, so
that Christian began to despair of life: but as
God would have it, while Apollyon was fetching
of his last blow, thereby to make a full end of
this good man, Christian nimbly stretched out
his hand for his sword, and caught it, saying,
" Rejoice not against me, O mine enemy: when
I fall I shall arise "; and with that gave him a
deadly thrust, which made him give back, as
one that had received his mortal wound. Christian
perceiving that, made at him again, saying,
" Nay, in all these things we are more than con-
querors through him that loved us." And with
that Apollyon spread forth his dragon's wings,

and sped him away, that Christian for a season saw him no more.

In this combat no man can imagine, unless he had seen and heard as I did, what yelling and hideous roaring Apollyon made all the time of the fight—he spake like a dragon; and, on the other side, what sighs and groans burst from Christian's heart. I never saw him all the while give so much as one pleasant look, till he perceived he had wounded Apollyon with his two-edged sword; then, indeed, he did smile, and look upward; but it was the dreadfullest sight that ever I saw.

So when the battle was over, Christian said, " I will here give thanks to him that delivered me out of the mouth of the lion, to him that did help me against Apollyon." And so he did.

Then there came to him a hand, with some of the leaves of the tree of life, the which Christian took, and applied to the wounds that he had received in the battle, and was healed immediately. He also sat down in that place to eat bread, and to drink of the bottle that was given him a little before; so, being refreshed, he addressed himself to his journey, with his sword drawn in his hand; for he said, I know not but some other enemy may be at hand. But he met with no other affront from Apollyon quite through this valley.

THE VALLEY OF THE SHADOW
OF DEATH

Now, at the end of this valley was another, called the Valley of the Shadow of Death, and Christian must needs go through it, because the way to the Celestial City lay through the midst of it. Now, this valley is a very solitary place. The prophet Jeremiah thus describes it: " A wilderness, a land of deserts and of pits, a land of drought, and of the shadow of death, a land that no man " (but a Christian) " passed through, and where no man dwelt."

Now here Christian was worse put to it than in his fight with Apollyon: as by the sequel you shall see.

I saw then in my dream, that when Christian was got to the borders of the Shadow of Death, there met him two men, children of them that brought up an evil report of the good land, making haste to go back; to whom Christian spake as follows:

Chr. Whither are you going?

Men. They said, Back! back! and we would

Evil report, etc. When Moses sent spies into Canaan to report about the country, all but two came back saying it was a very terrible country inhabited by giants, because they were afraid to go up against it and wanted to persuade the Israelites to go back.

have you to do so too, if either life or peace is prized by you.

Chr. Why, what's the matter? said Christian.

Men. Matter! said they; we were going that way as you are going, and went as far as we durst; and indeed we were almost past coming back; for had we gone a little further, we had not been here to bring the news to thee.

Chr. But what have you met with? said Christian.

Men. Why, we were almost in the Valley of the Shadow of Death; but that, by good hap, we looked before us, and saw the danger before we came to it.

Chr. But what have you seen? said Christian.

Men. Seen! Why, the Valley itself, which is as dark as pitch; we also saw there the hobgoblins, satyrs, and dragons of the pit; we heard also in that Valley a continual howling and yelling, as of a people under unutterable misery, who there sat bound in affliction and irons; and over that Valley hang the discouraging clouds of confusion. Death also doth always spread his wings over it. In a word, it is every whit dreadful, being utterly without order.

Chr. Then, said Christian, I perceive not yet, by what you have said, but that this is my way to the desired haven.

Men. Be it thy way; we will not choose it

for ours. So they parted, and Christian went on his way, but still with his sword drawn in his hand, for fear lest he should be assaulted.

I saw then in my dream so far as this valley reached, there was on the right hand a very deep ditch; that ditch is it into which the blind have led the blind in all ages, and have both there miserably perished. Again, behold, on the left hand, there was a very dangerous quag, into which, if even a good man falls, he can find no bottom for his foot to stand on.

The pathway was here also exceeding narrow, and therefore good Christian was the more put to it; for when he sought, in the dark, to shun the ditch on the one hand, he was ready to tip over into the mire on the other; also when he sought to escape the mire, without great carefulness he would be ready to fall into the ditch. Thus he went on, and I heard him here sigh bitterly; for, besides the dangers mentioned above, the pathway was here so dark, that ofttimes, when he lift up his foot to set forward, he knew not where or upon what he should set it next.

About the midst of this valley, I perceived the mouth of hell to be, and it stood also hard by the way-side. Now, thought Christian, what shall I do? And ever and anon the flame and smoke would come out in such abundance, with sparks and hideous noises (things that cared not

for Christian's sword, as did Apollyon before), that he was forced to put up his sword, and betake himself to another weapon, called All-prayer. So he cried in my hearing, " O Lord, I beseech thee, deliver my soul! " Thus he went on a great while, yet still the flames would be reaching towards him. Also he heard doleful voices, and rushings to and fro, so that some-times he thought he should be torn in pieces, or trodden down like mire in the streets. This frightful sight was seen, and these dreadful noises were heard by him for several miles together; and, coming to a place where he thought he heard a company of fiends coming forward to meet him, he stopped, and began to muse what he had best to do. Sometimes he had half a thought to go back; then again he thought he might be half way through the valley; he remembered also how he had already van-quished many a danger, and that the danger of going back might be much more than for to go forward; so he resolved to go on. Yet the fiends seemed to come nearer and nearer; but when they were come even almost at him, he cried out with a most vehement voice, " I will walk in the strength of the Lord God! " so they gave back, and came no further.

One thing I would not let slip; I took notice that now poor Christian was so confounded, that

he did not know his own voice ; and thus I perceived it. Just when he was come over against the mouth of the burning pit, one of the wicked ones got behind him, and stepped up softly to him, and whisperingly suggested many grievous blasphemies to him, which he verily thought had proceeded from his own mind. This put Christian more to it than anything that he met with before, even to think that he should now blaspheme him that he loved so much before; yet, if he could have helped it, he would not have done it; but he had not the discretion either to stop his ears, or to know from whence these blasphemies came.

When Christian had travelled in this disconsolate condition some considerable time, he thought he heard the voice of a man, as going before him, saying, " Though I walk through the valley of the shadow of death, I will fear no evil, for thou art with me."

Then he was glad, and that for these reasons:

First, Because he gathered from thence, that some who feared God were in this valley as well as himself.

Secondly, For that he perceived God was with them, though in that dark and dismal state; and why not, thought he, with me? though, by reason of the impediment that attends this place, I cannot perceive it.

Thirdly, For that he hoped, could he overtake them, to have company by and by. So he went on, and called to him that was before; but he knew not what to answer; for that he also thought himself to be alone; and by and by the day broke; then said Christian, He hath turned " the shadow of death into the morning."

Now morning being come, he looked back, not out of desire to return, but to see, by the light of the day, what hazards he had gone through in the dark. So he saw more perfectly the ditch that was on the one hand, and the quag that was on the other; also how narrow the way was which led betwixt them both; also now he saw the hobgoblins, and satyrs, and dragons of the pit, but all afar off (for after break of day, they came not nigh); yet they were discovered to him, according to that which is written, " He discovereth deep things out of darkness, and bringeth out to light the shadow of death."

Now was Christian much affected with his deliverance from all the dangers of his solitary way; which dangers, though he feared them more before, yet he saw them more clearly now, because the light of the day made them conspicuous to him. And about this time the sun was rising, and this was another mercy to Christian; for you must note, that though the first part of the Valley of the Shadow of Death

was dangerous, yet this second part which he
was yet to go, was, if possible, far more dangerous: for from the place where he now stood,
even to the end of the valley, the way was all
along set so full of snares, traps, gins, and nets
here, and so full of pits, pitfalls, deep holes, and
shelvings down there, that, had it now been dark,
as it was when he came the first part of the way,
had he had a thousand souls, they had in reason
been cast away; but, as I said just now, the sun
was rising. Then, said he, " His candle shineth
upon my head, and by his light I walk through
darkness."

CHRISTIAN MEETS WITH FAITHFUL

Now, as Christian went on his way, he came to
a little ascent, which was cast up on purpose
that pilgrims might see before them. Up there,
therefore, Christian went, and looking forward,
he saw Faithful before him, upon his journey.
Then said Christian aloud, " Ho! ho! Soho! stay,
and I will be your companion! " At that, Faithful looked behind him; to whom Christian cried
again, " Stay, stay, till I come up to you." But
Faithful answered, " No, I am upon my life, and
the avenger of blood is behind me."

At this, Christian was somewhat moved, and
putting to all his strength, he quickly got up with

Faithful, and did also overrun him; so the last was first. Then did Christian vain-gloriously smile, because he had gotten the start of his brother; but not taking good heed to his feet, he suddenly stumbled and fell, and could not rise again until Faithful came up to help him.

Then I saw in my dream they went very lovingly on together, and had sweet discourse of all things that had happened to them in their pilgrimage; and thus Christian began:

Chr. My honoured and well-beloved brother, Faithful, I am glad that I have overtaken you; and that God has so tempered our spirits, that we can walk as companions in this so pleasant a path.

Faith. I had thought, dear friend, to have had your company quite from our town; but you did get the start of me, wherefore I was forced to come thus much of the way alone.

Chr. How long did you stay in the City of Destruction, before you set out after me on your pilgrimage?

Faith. Till I could stay no longer; for there was great talk presently after you were gone out, that our city would, in short time, with fire from heaven, be burned down to the ground.

Chr. What! did your neighbours talk so?

Faith. Yes, it was for a while in everybody's mouth.

Chr. What! and did no more of them but you come out to escape the danger?

Faith. Though there was, as I said, a great talk thereabout, yet I do not think they did firmly believe it. For in the heat of the discourse, I heard some of them deridingly speak of you and of your desperate journey (for so they called this your pilgrimage), but I did believe, and do still, that the end of our city will be with fire and brimstone from above; and therefore I have made my escape.

Chr. Did you hear no talk of neighbour Pliable?

Faith. Yes, Christian, I heard that he followed you till he came at the Slough of Despond, where, as some said, he fell in; but he would not be known to have so done; but I am sure he was soundly bedabbled with that kind of dirt.

Chr. And what said the neighbours to him?

Faith. He hath, since his going back, been had greatly in derision, and that among all sorts of people; some do mock and despise him; and scarce will any set him on work. He is now seven times worse than if he had never gone out of the city.

Chr. But why should they be so set against him, since they also despise the way that he forsook?

Faith. Oh, they say, hang him, he is a turn-coat! he was not true to his profession. I think God has stirred up even his enemies to hiss at

him, and make him a proverb, because he hath
forsaken the way.

Chr. Had you no talk with him before you
came out?

Faith. I met him once in the streets, but he
leered away on the other side, as one ashamed
of what he had done; so I spake not to him.

Chr. Well, at my first setting out, I had hopes
of that man; but now I fear he will perish in
the overthrow of the city; for it is happened to
him according to the true proverb.

Faith. These are my fears of him too; but who
can hinder that which will be?

Chr. Well, neighbour Faithful, said Christian,
let us leave him, and talk of things that more
immediately concern ourselves. Tell me now,
what you have met with in the way as you came;
for I know you have met with some things, or
else it may be writ for a wonder.

Faith. I escaped the Slough that I perceived
you fell into, and got up to the gate without
that danger.

Chr. Did you meet with no other assault as
you came?

Faith. When I came to the foot of the hill
called Difficulty, I met with a very aged man,
who asked me what I was, and whither bound.
I told him that I am a pilgrim, going to the
Celestial City. Then said the old man, Thou

lookest like an honest fellow; wilt thou be content to dwell with me for the wages that I shall give thee? Then I asked him his name, and where he dwelt. He said his name was Adam the First, and that he dwelt in the town of Deceit. I asked him then what was his work, and what the wages that he would give. He told me, that his work was many delights; and his wages, that I should be his heir at last. I further asked him what house he kept, and what other servants he had. So he told me, that his house was maintained with all the dainties in the world; and that his servants were those of his own begetting. Then I asked if he had any children. He said that he had but three daughters: the Lust of the Flesh, the Lust of the Eyes, and the Pride of Life, and that I should marry them all if I would. Then I asked how long time he would have me live with him? And he told me, As long as he lived himself.

Chr. Well, and what conclusion came the old man and you to at last?

Faith. Why, at first, I found myself somewhat inclinable to go with the man, for I thought he spake very fair; but looking in his forehead, as I talked with him, I saw there written, " Put off the old man with his deeds."

Chr. And how then?

Faith. Then it came burning hot into my

D

mind, whatever he said, and however he flattered,
when he got me home to his house, he would sell
me for a slave. So I bid him forbear to talk, for
I would not come near the door of his house.
Then he reviled me, and told me that he would
send such a one after me, that should make my
way bitter to my soul. So I turned to go away
from him; but just as I turned myself to go
thence, I felt him take hold of my flesh, and
give me such a deadly twitch back, that I thought
he had pulled part of me after himself. This
made me cry, "Oh, wretched man!" So I went
on my way up the hill.

Now when I had got about half way up, I
looked behind, and saw one coming after me,
swift as the wind; so he overtook me just about
the place where the settle stands.

Chr. Just there, said Christian, did I sit down
to rest me; but being overcome with sleep, I
there lost this roll out of my bosom.

Faith. But, good brother, hear me out. So
soon as the man overtook me, he was but a word
and a blow, for down he knocked me, and laid
me for dead. But when I was a little come to
myself again, I asked him wherefore he served
me so. He said, because of my secret inclining
to Adam the First: and with that he struck me
another deadly blow on the breast, and beat
me down backward; so I lay at his foot as dead

as before. So, when I came to myself again, I cried him mercy; but he said, I know not how to show mercy; and with that knocked me down again. He had doubtless made an end of me, but that one came by, and bid him forbear.

Chr. Who was that that bid him forbear?

Faith. I did not know him at first, but as he went by, I perceived the holes in his hands and in his side; then I concluded that he was our Lord. So I went up the hill.

Chr. That man that overtook you was Moses. He spareth none, neither knoweth he how to show mercy to those that transgress his law.

Faith. I know it very well; it was not the first time that he has met with me.

Chr. But did you not see the house that stood there on the top of the hill, on the side of which Moses met you?

Faith. Yes, and the lions too, before I came at it: but for the lions, I think they were asleep, for it was about noon; and because I had so much of the day before me, I passed by the porter, and came down the hill.

Chr. He told me, indeed, that he saw you go by, but I wish you had called at the house, for they would have showed you so many rarities, that you would scarce have forgot them to the day of your death. But pray tell me, Did you meet nobody in the Valley of Humility?

Faith. Yes, I met with one Discontent, who would willingly have persuaded me to go back again with him; his reason was, for that the valley was altogether without honour. He told me, moreover, that there to go was the way to disobey all my friends, as Pride, Arrogancy, Self-conceit, Worldly-glory, with others, who, he knew, as he said, would be very much offended, if I made such a fool of myself as to wade through this valley.

Chr. Well, and how did you answer him?

Faith. I told him that although all these that he named might claim kindred of me, and that rightly, for indeed they were my relations according to the flesh; yet since I became a pilgrim, they have disowned me, as I also have rejected them; and therefore they were to me now no more than if they had never been of my lineage.

I told him, moreover, that as to this valley, he had quite misrepresented the thing; " for before honour is humility, and a haughty spirit before a fall." Therefore, said I, I had rather go through this valley to the honour that was so accounted by the wisest, than choose that which he esteemed most worthy our affections.

Chr. Met you with nothing else in that valley?

Faith. Yes, I met with Shame; but of all the men that I met with in my pilgrimage, he, I

think, bears the wrong name. The others would be said nay, after a little argumentation, and somewhat else; but this bold-faced Shame would never have done.

Chr. Why, what did he say to you?

Faith. What! why, he objected against religion itself; he said it was a pitiful, low, sneaking business, for a man to mind religion; he said that a tender conscience was an unmanly thing; and that for a man to watch over his words and ways, so as to tie up himself from that hectoring liberty that the brave spirits of the times accustom themselves unto, would make him the ridicule of the times. He objected also, that but few of the mighty, rich, or wise, were ever of my opinion. He, moreover, objected the base and low estate and condition of those that were chiefly the pilgrims of the times in which they lived: also their ignorance and want of understanding in all natural science. Yea, he did hold me to it at that rate also, about a great many more things than here I relate; as, that it was a *shame* to sit whining and mourning under a sermon, and a *shame* to come sighing and groaning home; that it was a *shame* to ask my neighbour forgiveness for petty faults, or to make restitution where I have taken from any. He said, also, that religion made a man grow strange to the great, because of a few vices, which he called by finer names;

and made him own and respect the base, because of the same religious fraternity. And is not this, said he, a *shame*?

Chr. And what did you say to him?

Faith. Say! I could not tell what to say at the first. Yea, he put me so to it, that my blood came up in my face ; even this Shame fetched it up, and had almost beat me quite off. But at last I began to consider, that " that which is highly esteemed among men, is had in abomination with God." And I thought again, This Shame tells me what men are; but it tells nothing what God or the Word of God is. And I thought, moreover, that at the day of doom, we shall not be doomed to death or life according to the hectoring spirits of the world, but according to the wisdom and law of the Highest. Therefore, thought I, what God says is best, indeed is best, though all the men in the world are against it. Seeing, then, that God prefers his religion; seeing God prefers a tender conscience; seeing they that make themselves fools for the kingdom of heaven are wisest; and that the poor man that loveth Christ is richer than the greatest man in the world that hates him; *Shame*, depart, thou art an enemy to my salvation! Shall I entertain thee against my sovereign Lord? How then shall I look him in the face at his coming? Should I now be ashamed of his ways and ser-

vants, how can I expect the blessing? But, indeed, this Shame was a bold villain; I could scarce shake him out of my company; yea, he would be haunting of me, and continually whispering me in the ear, with some one or other of the infirmities that attend religion; but at last I told him it was but in vain to attempt further in this business; for those things that he disdained, in those did I see most glory; and so at last I got past this importunate one. And when I had shaken him off, then I began to sing.

Chr. I am glad, my brother, that thou didst withstand this villain so bravely; for of all, as thou sayest, I think he has the wrong name; for he is so bold as to follow us in the streets, and to attempt to put us to shame before all men: that is, to make us ashamed of that which is good; but if he was not himself audacious, he would never attempt to do as he does. But let us still resist him; for notwithstanding all his bravadoes, he promoteth the fool and none else. "The wise shall inherit glory," said Solomon; "but shame shall be the promotion of fools."

Faith. I think we must cry to Him, for help against Shame, who would have us to be valiant for the truth upon the earth.

Chr. You say true; but did you meet nobody else in that valley?

Faith. No, not I; for I had sunshine all the

rest of the way through that, and also through the Valley of the Shadow of Death.

Chr. It was well for you. I am sure it fared far otherwise with me; I had for a long season, as soon almost as I entered into that valley, a dreadful combat with that foul fiend Apollyon; yea, I thought verily he would have killed me, especially when he got me down and crushed me under him, as if he would have crushed me to pieces; for as he threw me, my sword flew out of my hand; nay, he told me he was sure of me: but I cried to God, and he heard me, and delivered me out of all my troubles. Then I entered into the Valley of the Shadow of Death, and had no light for almost half the way through it. I thought I should have been killed there, over and over; but at last day broke, and the sun rose, and I went through that which was behind with far more ease and quiet.

THE PILGRIMS MEET WITH TALKATIVE

Moreover, I saw in my dream, that as they went on, Faithful, as he chanced to look on one side, saw a man whose name is Talkative, walking at a distance beside them; for in this place there was room enough for them all to walk. He was a tall man, and something more comely at a

distance than at hand. To this man Faithful addressed himself in this manner:

Faith. Friend, whither away? Are you going to the heavenly country?

Talk. I am going to the same place.

Faith. That is well; then I hope we may have your good company.

Talk. With a very good will will I be your companion.

Faith. Come on, then, and let us go together, and let us spend our time in discoursing of things that are profitable.

Talk. To talk of things that are good, to me is very acceptable, with you or with any other; and I am glad that I have met with those that incline to so good a work; for, to speak the truth, there are but few that care thus to spend their time (as they are in their travels), but choose much rather to be speaking of things to no profit; and this hath been a trouble to me.

Faith. That is indeed a thing to be lamented; for what things so worthy of the use of the tongue and mouth of men on earth, as are the things of the God of heaven?

Talk. I like you wonderful well, for your sayings are full of conviction; and I will add, what thing is so pleasant, and what so profitable, as to talk of the things of God? What things so pleasant (that is, if a man hath any delight in

*D

things that are wonderful)? For instance, if a man doth delight to talk of the history or the mystery of things; or if a man doth love to talk of miracles, wonders, or signs, where shall he find things recorded so delightful, and so sweetly penned, as in the Holy Scripture?

Faith. That is true; but to be profited by such things in our talk should be that which we design.

Talk. That is it that I said; for to talk of such things is most profitable: for by so doing, a man may get knowledge of many things; as of the vanity of earthly things, and the benefit of things above.

Faith. Well, then, said Faithful, what is that one thing that we shall at this time found our discourse upon?

Talk. What you will. I will talk of things heavenly, or things earthly; things moral, or things evangelical; things sacred, or things profane; things past, or things to come; things foreign, or things at home; things more essential, or things circumstantial; provided that all be done to our profit.

Faith. Now did Faithful begin to wonder; and stepping to Christian (for he walked all this while by himself), he said to him (but softly), What a brave companion have we got! Surely this man will make a very excellent pilgrim.

Chr. At this Christian modestly smiled, and

said, This man, with whom you are so taken, will beguile, with that tongue of his, twenty of them that know him not.

Faith. Do you know him then?

Chr. Know him! Yes, better than he knows himself.

Faith. Pray, what is he?

Chr. His name is Talkative; he dwelleth in our town. I wonder that you should be a stranger to him, only I consider that our town is large.

Faith. Whose son is he? And whereabout does he dwell?

Chr. He is the son of one Say-well; he dwelt in Prating Row; and is known of all that are acquainted with him, by the name of Talkative in Prating Row; and notwithstanding his fine tongue, he is but a sorry fellow.

Faith. Well, he seems to be a very pretty man.

Chr. That is, to them who have not thorough acquaintance with him; for he is best abroad; near home, he is ugly enough. Your saying that he is a pretty man, brings to my mind what I have observed in the work of the painter, whose pictures show best at a distance, but, very near, more unpleasing.

Faith. But I am ready to think you do but jest, because you smiled.

Chr. God forbid that I should jest (although I smiled) in this matter, or that I should accuse

any falsely! I will give you a further discovery of him. This man is for any company, and for any talk; as he talketh now with you, so will he talk when he is on the ale-bench; and the more drink he hath in his crown, the more of these things he hath in his mouth; religion hath no place in his heart, or house, or conversation; all he hath, lieth in his tongue, and his religion is, to make a noise therewith.

Faith. Say you so! then am I in this man greatly deceived.

Chr. Deceived! you may be sure of it; remember the proverb, " They say and do not." But the " kingdom of God is not in word, but in power." He talketh of prayer, of repentance, of faith, and of the new birth; but he knows but only to talk of them. I have been in his family, and have observed him both at home and abroad; and I know what I say of him is the truth. His house is as empty of religion as the white of an egg is of savour. There is there neither prayer, nor sign of repentance for sin; yea, the brute in his kind serves God far better than he. He is the very stain, reproach, and shame of religion, to all that know him; it can hardly have a good word in all that end of the town where he dwells, through him. Thus say the common people that know him, A saint abroad, and a devil at home. His poor family finds it so; he is such a churl,

such a railer at and so unreasonable with his servants, that they neither know how to do for, nor speak to him. Men that have any dealings with him, say it is better to deal with a Turk than with him; for fairer dealing they shall have at their hands. This Talkative (if it be possible) will go beyond them, defraud, beguile, and over-reach them. Besides, he brings up his sons to follow his steps; and if he findeth in any of them a foolish timorousness (for so he calls the first appearance of a tender conscience), he calls them fools and blockheads, and by no means will employ them in much, or speak to their com-mendations before others. For my part, I am of opinion, that he has, by his wicked life, caused many to stumble and fall; and will be, if God prevent not, the ruin of many more.

Faith. Well, my brother, I am bound to believe you; not only because you say you know him, but also because, like a Christian, you make your reports of men. For I cannot think that you speak these things of ill-will, but because it is even so as you say.

Chr. Had I known him no more than you, I might perhaps have thought of him, as, at the first, you did; yea, had he received this report at their hands only that are enemies to religion, I should have thought it had been a slander— a lot that often falls from bad men's mouths

upon good men's names and professions; but all these things, yea, and a great many more as bad, of my own knowledge, I can prove him guilty of. Besides, good men are ashamed of him; they can neither call him brother, nor friend; the very naming of him among them makes them blush, if they know him.

Faith. Well, I see that saying and doing are two things, and hereafter I shall better observe this distinction.

Chr. They are two things, indeed, and are as diverse as are the soul and the body; for as the body without the soul is but a dead carcass, so saying, if it be alone, is but a dead carcass also. The soul of religion is the practical part: " Pure religion and undefiled, before God and the Father, is this, to visit the fatherless and widows in their affliction, and to keep himself unspotted from the world." This Talkative is not aware of; he thinks that hearing and saying will make a good Christian, and thus he deceiveth his own soul. Hearing is but as the sowing of the seed; talking is not sufficient to prove that fruit is indeed in the heart and life; and let us assure ourselves, that at the day of doom men shall be judged according to their fruits. It will not be said then, Did you believe? but, Were you doers or talkers only? and accordingly shall they be judged.

Day of doom. Judgment day.

The end of the world is compared to our harvest; and you know men at harvest regard nothing but fruit.

Faith. Well, I was not so fond of his company at first, but I am as sick of it now. What shall we do to be rid of him?

Chr. Take my advice, and do as I bid you, and you shall find that he will soon be sick of your company too, except God shall touch his heart, and turn it.

Faith. What would you have me to do?

Chr. Why, go to him, and enter into some serious discourse about the power of religion; and ask him plainly (when he has approved of it, for that he will) whether this thing be set up in his heart, house, or conversation.

Faith. Then Faithful stepped forward again, and said to Talkative, Come, what cheer? How is it now?

Talk. Thank you, well. I thought we should have had a great deal of talk by this time.

But since you are ready to take up reports and to judge so rashly as you do, I cannot but conclude you are some peevish or melancholy man, not fit to be discoursed with; and so adieu.

Chr. Then came up Christian, and said to his brother, I told you how it would happen.

Thus they went on talking of what they had seen by the way, and so made that way easy

which would otherwise, no doubt, have been tedious to them; for now they went through a wilderness.

THE PILGRIMS ARE OVERTAKEN BY EVANGELIST

Now, when they were got almost quite out of this wilderness, Faithful chanced to cast his eye back, and espied one coming after them, and he knew him. Oh! said Faithful to his brother, Who comes yonder? Then Christian looked, and said, It is my good friend Evangelist. Ay, and my good friend too, said Faithful, for it was he that set me the way to the gate. Now was Evangelist come up to them, and thus saluted them:

Evan. Peace be with you, dearly beloved; and peace be to your helpers.

Chr. Welcome, welcome, my good Evangelist; the sight of thy countenance brings to my remembrance thy ancient kindness and unwearied labouring for my eternal good.

Faith. And a thousand times welcome, said good Faithful. Thy company, O sweet Evangelist, how desirable it is to us poor pilgrims!

Evan. Then said Evangelist, How hath it fared with you, my friends, since the time of our last

parting? What have you met with, and how have you behaved yourselves?

Then Christian and Faithful told him of all things that had happened to them in the way; and how, and with what difficulty, they had arrived to that place.

Evan. Right glad am I, said Evangelist, not that you have met with trials, but that you have been victors; and for that you have, notwithstanding many weaknesses, continued in the way to this very day.

I say, right glad am I of this thing, and that for mine own sake and yours. I have sowed, and you have reaped: and the day is coming, when both he that sowed and they that reaped shall rejoice together; that is, if you hold out: "for in due season ye shall reap, if ye faint not." The crown is before you, and it is an incorruptible one; "so run, that you may obtain it." Some there be that set out for this crown, and, after they have gone far for it, another comes in, and takes it from them: hold fast, therefore, that you have; let no man take your crown. You are not yet out of the gun-shot of the devil; you have not resisted unto blood, striving against sin; let the kingdom be always before you, and believe steadfastly concerning things that are invisible. Let nothing that is on this side the other world get within you; and, above all, look well to your

own hearts, and to the lusts thereof, " for they are deceitful above all things, and desperately wicked "; set your faces like a flint; you have all power in heaven and earth on your side.

Then Christian thanked him for his exhortation; but told him, withal, that they would have him speak further to them for their help the rest of the way, and the rather, for that they well knew that he was a prophet, and could tell them of things that might happen unto them, and also how they might resist and overcome them. To which request Faithful also consented. So Evangelist began as followeth:

Evan. My sons, you have heard, in the words of the truth of the gospel, that you must, through many tribulations, enter into the kingdom of heaven. And, again, that in every city bonds and afflictions abide in you; and therefore you cannot expect that you should go long on your pilgrimage without them, in some sort or other. You have found something of the truth of these testimonies upon you already, and more will immediately follow; for now, as you see, you are almost out of this wilderness, and therefore you will soon come into a town that you will by and by see before you; and in that town you will be hardly beset with enemies, who will strain hard but they will kill you; and be you sure that one or both of you must seal the testimony

which you hold, with blood; but be you faithful unto death, and the King will give you a crown of life. He that shall die there, although his death will be unnatural, and his pain perhaps great, he will yet have the better of his fellow; not only because he will be arrived at the Celestial City soonest, but because he will escape many miseries that the other will meet with in the rest of his journey. But when you are come to the town, and shall find fulfilled what I have here related, then remember your friend, and quit yourselves like men, and commit the keeping of your souls to your God in well-doing, as unto a faithful Creator.

VANITY FAIR

Then I saw in my dream, that when they were got out of the wilderness, they presently saw a town before them, and the name of that town is Vanity; and at the town there is a fair kept, called Vanity Fair: it is kept all the year long; it beareth the name of Vanity Fair, because the town where it is kept is lighter than vanity; and also because all that is there sold, or that cometh thither, is vanity.

This fair is no new-erected business, but a thing of ancient standing; I will show you the original of it.

Almost five thousand years agone, there were pilgrims walking to the Celestial City, as these two honest persons are: and Beelzebub, Apollyon, and Legion, with their companions, perceiving by the path that the pilgrims made, that their way to the city lay through this town of Vanity, they contrived here to set up a fair; a fair wherein should be sold all sorts of vanity, and that it should last all the year long: therefore at this fair are all such merchandise sold, as houses, lands, trades, places, honours, preferments, titles, countries, kingdoms, lusts, pleasures, and delights of all sorts, as lovers, wives, husbands, children, masters, servants, lives, blood, bodies, souls, silver, gold, pearls, precious stones, and what not.

And, moreover, at this fair there is at all times to be seen juggling, cheats, games, plays, fools, apes, knaves, and rogues, and that of every kind.

And as in other fairs of less moment, there are the several rows and streets, under their proper names, where such and such wares are vended; so here likewise you have the proper places, rows, streets (viz. countries and kingdoms), where the wares of this fair are soonest to be found. Here is the Britain Row, the French Row, the Italian Row, the Spanish Row, the German Row, where several sorts of vanities are to be sold. But, as in other fairs, some one commodity is as the chief of all the fair, so the ware of Rome and her

merchandise is greatly promoted in this fair; only our English nation, with some others, have taken a dislike thereat.

Now, as I said, the way to the Celestial City lies just through this town where this lusty fair is kept; and he that will go to the City, and yet not go through this town, must needs "go out of the world." The Prince of princes himself, when here, went through this town to his own country, and that upon a fair day too; yea, and as I think, it was Beelzebub, the chief lord of this fair, that invited him to buy of his vanities; yea, would have made him lord of the fair, would he but have done him reverence as he went through the town. Yea, because he was such a person of honour, Beelzebub had him from street to street, and showed him all the kingdoms of the world in a little time, that he might, if possible, allure the Blessed One to cheapen and buy some of his vanities; but he had no mind to the merchandise, and therefore left the town, without laying out so much as one farthing upon these vanities. This fair, therefore, is an ancient thing, of long standing, and a very great fair. Now these pilgrims, as I said, must needs go through this fair. Well, so they did: but, behold, even as they entered into the fair, all the people in the fair were moved, and the town itself as it

Cheapen. Bargain for.

were in a hubbub about them; and that for several reasons: for—

First, The pilgrims were clothed with such kind of raiment as was diverse from the raiment of any that traded in that fair. The people, therefore, of the fair made a great gazing upon them: some said they were fools, some they were bedlams, and some they were outlandish men.

Secondly, And as they wondered at their apparel, so they did likewise at their speech; for few could understand what they said; they naturally spoke the language of Canaan, but they that kept the fair were the men of this world; so that, from one end of the fair to the other, they seemed barbarians each to the other.

Thirdly, But that which did not a little amuse the merchandisers was, that these pilgrims set very light by all their wares; they cared not so much as to look upon them; and if they called upon them to buy, they would put their fingers in their ears, and cry, " Turn away mine eyes from beholding vanity," and look upwards, signifying that their trade and traffic was in heaven.

One chanced mockingly, beholding the carriage

Bedlams. Hospitals for mad people were called Bethlehems from one dedicated to " St. Mary of Bethlehem." This got shortened in speaking to Bedlam, and mad people were often called bedlams.

Carriage. General appearance and way of bearing oneself.

of the men, to say unto them, What will ye buy? But they, looking gravely upon him, answered, "We buy the truth." At that there was an occasion taken to despise the men the more; some mocking, some taunting, some speaking reproachfully, and some calling upon others to smite them. At last things came to a hubbub and great stir in the fair, insomuch that all order was confounded. Now was word presently brought to the great one of the fair, who quickly came down, and deputed some of his most trusty friends to take these men into examination, about whom the fair was almost overturned. So the men were brought to examination; and they that sat upon them, asked them whence they came, whither they went, and what they did there, in such an unusual garb? The men told them that they were pilgrims and strangers in the world, and that they were going to their own country, which was the heavenly Jerusalem; and that they had given no occasion to the men of the town, nor yet to the merchandisers, thus to abuse them, and to let them in their journey, except it was for that, when one asked them what they would buy, they said they would buy the truth. But they that were appointed to examine them did not believe them to be any other than bedlams and mad, or else such as

Let them in their journey. Prevent or stand in the way of.

came to put all things into a confusion in the
fair. Therefore they took them and beat them,
and besmeared them with dirt, and then put
them into the cage, that they might be made
a spectacle to all the men of the fair.

There, therefore, they lay for some time, and
were made the objects of any man's sport, or
malice, or revenge, the great one of the fair
laughing still at all that befell them. But the
men being patient, and not rendering railing
for railing, but contrariwise, blessing, and giving
good words for bad, and kindness for injuries
done, some men in the fair that were more
observing, and less prejudiced than the rest,
began to check and blame the baser sort for
their continual abuses done by them to the men;
they, therefore, in angry manner, let fly at them
again, counting them as bad as the men in the
cage, and telling them that they seemed con-
federates, and should be made partakers of their
misfortunes. The other replied, that for aught
they could see, the men were quiet, and sober,
and intended nobody any harm; and that there
were many that traded in their fair that were
more worthy to be put into the cage, yea, and
pillory too, than were the men they had abused.
Thus, after divers words had passed on both
sides, the men behaving themselves all the while
very wisely and soberly before them, they fell

to some blows among themselves, and did harm
one to another. Then were these two poor men
brought before their examiners again, and there
charged as being guilty of the late hubbub that
had been in the fair. So they beat them pitifully,
and hanged irons upon them, and led them in
chains up and down the fair, for an example
and a terror to others, lest any should speak in
their behalf, or join themselves unto them. But
Christian and Faithful behaved themselves yet
more wisely, and received the ignominy and
shame that was cast upon them, with so much
meekness and patience, that it won to their side,
though but few in comparison of the rest, several
of the men in the fair. This put the other party
yet into greater rage, insomuch that they concluded the death of these two men. Wherefore
they threatened, that neither cage nor irons
should serve their turn, but that they should die,
for the abuse they had done, and for deluding
the men of the fair.

Then were they remanded to the cage again,
until further order should be taken with them.
So they put them in, and made their feet fast
in the stocks.

Here, therefore, they called again to mind
what they had heard from their faithful friend
Evangelist, and were the more confirmed in their
way and sufferings, by what he told them would

happen to them. They also now comforted each other, that whose lot it was to suffer, even he should have the best of it; therefore each man secretly wished that he might have that preferment: but committing themselves to the allwise disposal of Him that ruleth all things, with much content, they abode in the condition in which they were, until they should be otherwise disposed of.

THE TRIAL BEFORE LORD HATE-GOOD AND THE DEATH OF FAITHFUL

Then a convenient time being appointed, they brought them forth to their trial, in order to their condemnation. When the time was come, they were brought before their enemies and arraigned. The Judge's name was Lord Hategood. Their indictment was one and the same in substance, though somewhat varying in form, the contents whereof were this:

"That they were enemies to and disturbers of their trade; that they had made commotions and divisions in the town, and had won a party to their own most dangerous opinions, in contempt of the law of their prince."

Then Faithful began to answer, that he had only set himself against that which hath set itself against Him that is higher than the highest.

And, said he, as for disturbance, I make none, being myself a man of peace; the parties that were won to us, were won by beholding our truth and innocence, and they are only turned from the worse to the better. And as to the king you talk of, since he is Beelzebub, the enemy of our Lord, I defy him and all his angels.

Then proclamation was made, that they that had aught to say for their lord the king against the prisoner at the bar, should forthwith appear and give in their evidence. So there came in three witnesses, to wit, Envy, Superstition, and Pickthank. They were then asked if they knew the prisoner at the bar; and what they had to say for their lord the king against him.

Then stood forth Envy, and said to this effect: My Lord, I have known this man a long time, and will attest upon my oath before this honourable bench that he is——

Judge. Hold! Give him his oath. (So they sware him.) Then he said—

Envy. My Lord, this man, notwithstanding his plausible name, is one of the vilest men in our country. He neither regardeth prince nor people, law nor custom; but doth all that he can to possess all men with certain of his disloyal notions, which he in the general calls principles of faith and holiness. And, in particular, I heard him once myself affirm that Christianity and the

customs of our town of Vanity were diametrically opposite, and could not be reconciled. By which saying, my Lord, he doth at once not only condemn all our laudable doings, but us in the doing of them.

Judge. Then did the Judge say to him, Hast thou any more to say?

Envy. My Lord, I could say much more, only I would not be tedious to the court. Yet, if need be, when the other gentlemen have given in their evidence, rather than anything shall be wanting that will despatch him, I will enlarge my testimony against him. So he was bid to stand by.

Then they called Superstition, and bid him look upon the prisoner. They also asked, what he could say for their lord the king against him. Then they sware him; so he began.

Super. My Lord, I have no great acquaintance with this man, nor do I desire to have further knowledge of him; however, this I know, that he is a very pestilent fellow, from some discourse that, the other day, I had with him in this town; for then, talking with him, I heard him say, that our religion was nought, and such by which a man could by no means please God. Which sayings of his, my Lord, your Lordship very well knows, what necessarily thence will follow, to wit, that we do still worship in vain, are yet in

our sins, and finally shall be damned; and this is that which I have to say.

Then was Pickthank sworn, and bid say what he knew, in behalf of their lord the king, against the prisoner at the bar.

Pick. My Lord, and you gentlemen all, This fellow I have known of a long time, and have heard him speak things that ought not to be spoke; for he hath railed on our noble prince Beelzebub, and hath spoken contemptibly of his honourable friends, whose names are the Lord Old Man, the Lord Carnal Delight, the Lord Luxurious, the Lord Desire of Vain Glory, my old Lord Lechery, Sir Having Greedy, with all the rest of our nobility; and he hath said, moreover, That if all men were of his mind, if possible, there is not one of these noblemen should have any longer a being in this town. Besides, he hath not been afraid to rail on you, my Lord, who are now appointed to be his judge, calling you an ungodly villain, with many other such like vilifying terms, with which he hath bespattered most of the gentry of our town.

When this Pickthank had told his tale, the Judge directed his speech to the prisoner at the bar, saying, Thou runagate, heretic, and traitor, hast thou heard what these honest gentlemen have witnessed against thee?

Runagate, or renegade. Betrayer.

Faith. May I speak a few words in my own defence?

Judge. Sirrah! Sirrah! thou deservest to live no longer, but to be slain immediately upon the place; yet, that all men may see our gentleness towards thee, let us hear what thou, vile runagate, hast to say.

Faith. 1. I say, then, in answer to what Mr. Envy hath spoken, I never said aught but this, That what rule, or laws, or customs, or people, were flat against the Word of God, are diametrically opposite to Christianity. If I have said amiss in this, convince me of my error, and I am ready here before you to make my recantation.

2. As to the second, to wit, Mr. Superstition, and his charge against me, I said only this, That in the worship of God there is required a Divine faith; but there can be no Divine faith without a Divine revelation of the will of God. Therefore, whatever is thrust into the worship of God that is not agreeable to Divine revelation, cannot be done but by a human faith, which faith will not be profitable to eternal life.

3. As to what Mr. Pickthank hath said, I say (avoiding terms, as that I am said to rail, and the like), That the prince of this town, with all the rabblement, his attendants, by this gentleman named, are more fit for a being in hell, than

in this town and country: and so, the Lord have mercy upon me!

Then the Judge called to the jury (who all this while stood by, to hear and observe): Gentlemen of the jury, you see this man about whom so great an uproar hath been made in this town. You have also heard what these worthy gentlemen have witnessed against him. Also you have heard his reply and confession. It lieth now in your breasts to hang him or save his life; but yet I think meet to instruct you into our law.

There was an Act made in the days of Pharaoh the Great, servant to our prince, that lest those of a contrary religion should multiply and grow too strong for him, their males should be thrown into the river. There was also an Act made in the days of Nebuchadnezzar the Great, another of his servants, that whosoever would not fall down and worship his golden image, should be thrown into a fiery furnace. There was also an Act made in the days of Darius, that whoso, for some time, called upon any god but him, should be cast into the lions' den. Now the substance of these laws this rebel has broken, not only in thought (which is not to be borne), but also in word and deed; which must therefore needs be intolerable.

Then went the jury out, whose names were, Mr. Blind-man, Mr. No-good, Mr. Malice, Mr.

Love-lust, Mr. Live-loose, Mr. Heady, Mr. High-mind, Mr. Enmity, Mr. Liar, Mr. Cruelty, Mr. Hate-light, and Mr. Implacable; who every one gave in his private verdict against him among themselves, and afterwards unanimously concluded to bring him in guilty before the Judge. And first, among themselves, Mr. Blind-man, the foreman, said, I see clearly that this man is a heretic. Then said Mr. No-good, Away with such a fellow from the earth. Ay, said Mr. Malice, for I hate the very looks of him. Then said Mr. Love-lust, I could never endure him. Nor I, said Mr. Live-loose, for he would always be condemning my way. Hang him, hang him, said Mr. Heady. A sorry scrub, said Mr. High-mind. My heart riseth against him, said Mr. Enmity. He is a rogue, said Mr. Liar. Hanging is too good for him, said Mr. Cruelty. Let us despatch him out of the way, said Mr. Hate-light. Then said Mr. Implacable, Might I have all the world given me, I could not be reconciled to him; therefore, let us forthwith bring him in guilty of death. And so they did; therefore he was presently condemned to be had from the place where he was, to the place from whence he came, and there to be put to the most cruel death that could be invented.

They, therefore, brought him out, to do with him according to their law; and, first, they

scourged him, then they buffeted him, then they lanced his flesh with knives; after that, they stoned him with stones, then pricked him with their swords; and, last of all, they burned him to ashes at the stake. Thus came Faithful to his end.

Now I saw that there stood behind the multitude a chariot and a couple of horses, waiting for Faithful, who (so soon as his adversaries had despatched him) was taken up into it, and straightway was carried up through the clouds, with sound of trumpet, the nearest way to the celestial gate.

CHRISTIAN ESCAPES AND MEETS WITH BY-ENDS

But as for Christian, he had some respite, and was remanded back to prison. So he there remained for a space; but He that overrules all things, having the power of their rage in his own hand, so wrought it about, that Christian for that time escaped them, and went his way.

Now I saw in my dream, that Christian went not forth alone, for there was one whose name was Hopeful (being made so by the beholding of Christian and Faithful in their words and behaviour, in their sufferings at the Fair), who joined himself unto him, and, entering into a brotherly covenant, told him that he would be

E

his companion. Thus, one died to bear testimony to the truth, and another rises out of his ashes, to be a companion with Christian in his pilgrimage. This Hopeful also told Christian, that there were many more of the men in the Fair, that would take their time and follow after.

So I saw that quickly after they were got out of the Fair, they overtook one that was going before them, whose name was By-ends: so they said to him, What countryman, Sir? and how far go you this way? He told them that he came from the town of Fair-speech, and he was going to the Celestial City, but told them not his name.

From Fair-speech! said Christian. Is there any good that lives there?

By-ends. Yes, said By-ends, I hope.

Chr. Pray, Sir, what may I call you? said Christian.

By-ends. I am a stranger to you, and you to me: if you be going this way, I shall be glad of your company; if not, I must be content.

Chr. This town of Fair-speech, said Christian, I have heard of; and, as I remember, they say, it is a wealthy place.

By-ends. Yes, I will assure you that it is; and I have very many rich kindred there.

Chr. Pray, who are your kindred there? if a man may be so bold.

By-ends. Almost the whole town; and in

particular, my Lord Turn-about, my Lord Time-server, my Lord Fair-speech (from whose ancestors that town first took its name), also Mr. Smooth-man, Mr. Facing-both-ways, Mr. Anything; and the parson of our parish, Mr. Two-tongues, was my mother's own brother by father's side; and to tell you the truth, I am become a gentleman of good quality, yet my great-grandfather was but a waterman, looking one way and rowing another, and I got most of my estate by the same occupation.

Chr. Are you a married man?

By-ends. Yes, and my wife is a very virtuous woman, the daughter of a virtuous woman; she was my Lady Feigning's daughter, therefore she came of a very honourable family, and is arrived to such a pitch of breeding, that she knows how to carry it to all, even to prince and peasant. It is true we somewhat differ in religion from those of the stricter sort, yet but in two small points: first, we never strive against wind and tide; secondly, we are always most zealous when religion goes in his silver slippers; we love much to walk with him in the street, if the sun shines, and the people applaud him.

Then Christian stepped a little aside to his fellow, Hopeful, saying, It runs in my mind that this is one By-ends of Fair-speech; and if it be

Carry it to all. Behave herself to all.

he, we have as very a knave in our company as dwelleth in all these parts. Then said Hopeful, Ask him; methinks he should not be ashamed of his name. So Christian came up with him again, and said, Sir, you talk as if you knew something more than all the world doth; and if I take not my mark amiss, I deem I have half a guess of you: Is not your name Mr. By-ends, of Fair-speech?

By-ends. This is not my name, but indeed it is a nickname that is given me by some that cannot abide me: and I must be content to bear it as a reproach, as other good men have borne theirs before me.

Chr. But did you never give an occasion to men to call you by this name?

By-ends. Never, never! The worst that ever I did to give them an occasion to give me this name was, that I had always the luck to jump in my judgment with the present way of the times, whatever it was, and my chance was to get thereby; but if things are thus cast upon me, let me count them a blessing; but let not the malicious load me therefore with reproach.

Chr. I thought, indeed, that you were the man that I heard of; and to tell you what I

If I take not my mark amiss. If I have aimed (guessed) rightly.

Jump. Agree.

think, I fear this name belongs to you more properly than you are willing we should think it doth.

By-ends. Well, if you will thus imagine, I cannot help it; you shall find me a fair company-keeper, if you will still admit me your associate.

Chr. If you will go with us, you must go against the wind and tide; the which, I perceive, is against your opinion; you must also own religion in his rags, as well as when in his silver slippers; and stand by him, too, when bound in irons, as well as when he walketh the streets with applause.

By-ends. You must not impose, nor lord it over my faith; leave me to my liberty, and let me go with you.

Chr. Not a step further, unless you will do in what I propound as we.

Then said By-ends, I shall never desert my old principles, since they are harmless and profitable. If I may not go with you, I must do as I did before you overtook me, even go by myself, until some overtake me that will be glad of my company.

BY-ENDS FINDS CONGENIAL COMPANY

Now I saw in my dream, that Christian and Hopeful forsook him, and kept their distance before him; but one of them looking back, saw

three men following Mr. By-ends, and behold, as they came up with him, he made them a very low *congé*; and they also gave him a compliment. The men's names were Mr. Hold-the-world, Mr. Money-love, and Mr. Save-all; men that Mr. By-ends had formerly been acquainted with; for in their minority they were schoolfellows, and were taught by one Mr. Gripe-man, a schoolmaster in Love-gain, which is a market town in the county of Coveting, in the north. This schoolmaster taught them the art of getting, either by violence, cozenage, flattery, lying, or by putting on a guise of religion; and these four gentlemen had attained much of the art of their master, so that they could each of them have kept such a school themselves.

Well, when they had, as I said, thus saluted each other, Mr. Money-love said to Mr. By-ends, Who are they upon the road before us? (for Christian and Hopeful were yet within view).

By-ends. They are a couple of far countrymen, that, after their mode, are going on pilgrimage.

Money-love. Alas! Why did they not stay, that we might have had their good company? for they, and we, and you, Sir, I hope, are all going on a pilgrimage.

Congé. Bow; literally, leave. (**You said as you bowed, "By your leave."**)
Cozenage. Cheating, deceit.

By-ends. We are so, indeed; but the men before us are so rigid, and love so much their own notions, and do also so lightly esteem the opinions of others, that let a man be never so godly, yet if he jumps not with them in all things, they thrust him quite out of their company.

Save-all. That is bad, but we read of some that are righteous overmuch; and such men's rigidness prevails with them to judge and condemn all but themselves. But, I pray, what, and how many, were the things wherein you differed?

By-ends. Why, they, after their headstrong manner, conclude that it is duty to rush on their journey all weathers; and I am for waiting for wind and tide. They are for hazarding all for God at a clap; and I am for taking all advantages to secure my life and estate. They are for holding their notions, though all other men are against them; but I am for religion in what, and so far as the times, and my safety, will bear it. They are for religion when in rags and contempt; but I am for him when he walks in his golden slippers, in the sunshine, and with applause.

Mr. Hold-the-world. Ay, and hold you there still, good Mr. By-ends; for, for my part, I can count him but a fool, that, having the liberty to keep what he has, shall be so unwise as to lose it. Let us be wise as serpents; it is best to

make hay when the sun shines; you see how the bee lieth still all winter, and bestirs her only when she can have profit with pleasure. God sends sometimes rain, and sometimes sunshine; if they be such fools to go through the first, yet let us be content to take fair weather along with us.

THE PILGRIMS MEET DEMAS

Then Christian and Hopeful went till they came at a delicate plain called Ease, where they went with much content; but that plain was but narrow, so they were quickly got over it. Now at the further side of that plain was a little hill called Lucre, and in that hill a silver mine, which some of them that had formerly gone that way, because of the rarity of it, had turned aside to see; but going too near the brink of the pit, the ground being deceitful under them, broke, and they were slain; some also had been maimed there, and could not, to their dying day, be their own men again.

Then I saw in my dream, that a little off the road, over against the silver mine, stood Demas

---

Delicate. Delightful, pleasant, delicious.

Demas. He was a fellow-worker with St. Paul, but forsook him, "having loved the present world." He stands for those who are tempted by the riches of this life to turn aside from their pilgrimage.

(gentleman-like) to call to passengers to come and see; who said to Christian and his fellow, Ho! turn aside hither, and I will show you a thing.

Chr. What thing so deserving as to turn us out of the way to see it?

Demas. Here is a silver mine, and some digging in it for treasure. If you will come, with a little pains you may richly provide for yourselves.

Hope. Then said Hopeful, Let us go see.

Chr. Not I, said Christian, I have heard of this place before now; and how many have there been slain; and besides that, treasure is a snare to those that seek it; for it hindereth them in their pilgrimage. Then Christian called to Demas, saying, Is not the place dangerous? Hath it not hindered many in their pilgrimage?

Demas. Not very dangerous, except to those that are careless (but withal, he blushed as he spake).

Chr. Then said Christian to Hopeful, Let us not stir a step, but still keep on our way.

Hope. I will warrant you, when By-ends comes up, if he hath the same invitation as we, he will turn in thither to see.

Chr. No doubt thereof, for his principles lead him that way, and a hundred to one but he dies there.

Demas. Then Demas called again, saying, But will you not come over and see?

Chr. Then Christian roundly answered, saying,

*E

Demas, thou art an enemy to the right ways of
the Lord of this way, and hast been already
condemned for thine own turning aside, by one
of his Majesty's judges; and why seekest thou
to bring us into the like condemnation? Besides,
if we at all turn aside, our Lord the King will
certainly hear thereof, and will there put us to
shame, where we would stand with boldness
before him. Thus they went their way.

By this time By-ends and his companions
were come again within sight, and they, at the
first beck, went over to Demas. Now, whether
they fell into the pit by looking over the brink
thereof, or whether they went down to dig, or
whether they were smothered in the bottom by
the damps that commonly arise, of these things
I am not certain; but this I observed, that they
never were seen again in the way.

LOT'S WIFE

Now I saw that, just on the other side of this
plain, the pilgrims came to a place where stood
an old monument, hard by the highway side,
at the sight of which they were both concerned,
because of the strangeness of the form thereof;
for it seemed to them as if it had been a woman
transformed into the shape of a pillar; here
therefore they stood looking, and looking upon

it, but could not for a time tell what they should make thereof. At last Hopeful espied written above the head thereof, a writing in an unusual hand; but he being no scholar, called to Christian (for he was learned) to see if he could pick out the meaning; so he came, and after a little laying of letters together, he found the same to be this, "Remember Lot's wife." So he read it to his fellow; after which they both concluded that that was the pillar of salt into which Lot's wife was turned, for her looking back with a covetous heart, when she was going from Sodom for safety. Which sudden and amazing sight gave them occasion of this discourse.

Chr. Ah, my brother! this is a seasonable sight; it came opportunely to us after the invitation which Demas gave us to come over to view the Hill Lucre; and had we gone over, as he desired us, and as thou wast inclining to do, my brother, we had, for aught I know, been made ourselves like this woman, a spectacle for those that shall come after to behold.

Hope. I am sorry that I was so foolish, and am made to wonder that I am not now as Lot's wife; for wherein was the difference betwixt her sin and mine? She only looked back; and I had a desire to go see. Let grace be adored, and let me be ashamed that ever such a thing should be in mine heart.

THE RIVER OF LIFE

I saw, then, that they went on their way to a pleasant river; which David the king called "the river of God," but John, "the river of the water of life." Now their way lay just upon the bank of the river; here, therefore, Christian and his companion walked with great delight; they drank also of the water of the river, which was pleasant, and enlivening to their weary spirits: besides, on the banks of this river, on either side, were green trees, that bore all manner of fruit; and the leaves of the trees were good for medicine; with the fruit of these trees they were also much delighted; and the leaves they ate to prevent surfeits, and other diseases that are incident to those that heat their blood by travels. On either side of the river was also a meadow, curiously beautified with lilies, and it was green all the year long. In this meadow they lay down, and slept; for here they might lie down safely. When they awoke, they gathered again of the fruit of the trees, and drank again of the water of the river, and then lay down again to sleep. Thus they did several days and nights.

So when they were disposed to go on (for they were not, as yet, at their journey's end), they ate and drank, and departed.

BY-PATH MEADOW

Now, I beheld in my dream, that they had not journeyed far, but the river and the way for a time parted; at which they were not a little sorry; yet they durst not go out of the way. Now the way from the river was rough, and their feet tender, by reason of their travels; " so the souls of the pilgrims were much discouraged because of the way." Wherefore, still as they went on, they wished for better way. Now, a little before them, there was on the left hand of the road a meadow, and a stile to go over into it; and that meadow is called By-path Meadow. Then said Christian to his fellow, If this meadow lieth along by our wayside, let us go over into it. Then he went to the stile to see, and behold, a path lay along by the way, on the other side of the fence. It is according to my wish, said Christian. Here is the easiest going; come, good Hopeful, and let us go over.

Hope. But how if this path should lead us out of the way?

Chr. That is not like, said the other. Look, doth it not go along by the wayside? So Hopeful, being persuaded by his fellow, went after him over the stile. When they were gone over, and were got into the path, they found it very easy for their feet; and withal, they, looking

before them, espied a man walking as they did (and his name was Vain-confidence); so they called after him, and asked him whither that way led. He said, To the Celestial Gate. Look, said Christian, did not I tell you so? By this you may see we are right. So they followed, and he went before them. But, behold, the night came on, and it grew very dark; so that they that were behind lost the sight of him that went before.

He, therefore, that went before (Vain-confidence by name), not seeing the way before him, fell into a deep pit, which was on purpose there made, by the Prince of those grounds, to catch vain-glorious fools withal, and was dashed in pieces with his fall.

Now Christian and his fellow heard him fall. So they called to know the matter, but there was none to answer, only they heard a groaning. Then said Hopeful, Where are we now? Then was his fellow silent, as mistrusting that he had led him out of the way; and now it began to rain, and thunder, and lighten in a very dreadful manner; and the water rose amain.

Then Hopeful groaned in himself, saying, Oh, that I had kept on my way!

Chr. Who could have thought that this path should have led us out of the way?

Hope. I was afraid on it at the very first, and

therefore gave you that gentle caution. I would have spoken plainer, but that you are older than I.

Chr. Good brother, be not offended; I am sorry I have brought thee out of the way, and that I have put thee into such imminent danger; pray, my brother, forgive me; I did not do it of an evil intent.

Hope. Be comforted, my brother, for I forgive thee; and believe, too, that this shall be for our good.

Chr. I am glad I have with me a merciful brother; but we must not stand thus: let us try to go back again.

Hope. But, good brother, let me go before.

Chr. No, if you please, let me go first, that if there be any danger, I may be first therein, because by my means we are both gone out of the way.

Hope. No, said Hopeful, you shall not go first; for your mind being troubled may lead you out of the way again. Then, for their encouragement, they heard the voice of one saying, " Set thine heart toward the highway, even the way which thou wentest; turn again." But by this time the waters were greatly risen, by reason of which the way of going back was very dangerous. (Then I thought that it is easier going out of the way, when we are in, than going in when we

are out.) Yet they adventured to go back, but it was so dark, and the flood was so high, that in their going back they had like to have been drowned nine or ten times.

Neither could they, with all the skill they had, get again to the stile that night. Wherefore, at last, lighting under a little shelter, they sat down there until the day-break; but, being weary, they fell asleep.

DOUBTING CASTLE

Now there was, not far from the place where they lay, a castle called Doubting Castle, the owner whereof was Giant Despair; and it was in his grounds they now were sleeping: wherefore he, getting up in the morning early, and walking up and down in his fields, caught Christian and Hopeful asleep in his grounds. Then, with a grim and surly voice, he bid them awake; and asked them whence they were, and what they did in his grounds. They told him they were pilgrims, and that they had lost their way. Then said the Giant, You have this night trespassed on me, by trampling in and lying on my grounds, and therefore you must go along with me. So they were forced to go, because he was stronger than they. They also had but little to say, for they knew themselves in a fault. The

CHRISTIAN AND HOPEFUL ARE LOCKED UP
BY GIANT DESPAIR

CHRISTIAN AND HOPEFUL ARE LOCKED UP
BY GIANT DESPAIR

Giant, therefore, drove them before him, and put them into his castle, into a very dark dungeon, nasty and stinking to the spirits of these two men. Here, then, they lay from Wednesday morning till Saturday night, without one bit of bread, or drop of drink, or light, or any to ask how they did; they were, therefore, here in evil case, and were far from friends and acquaintance. Now in this place Christian had double sorrow, because it was through his unadvised counsel that they were brought into this distress.

Now, Giant Despair had a wife, and her name was Diffidence. So when he was gone to bed, he told his wife what he had done; to wit, that he had taken a couple of prisoners and cast them into his dungeon, for trespassing on his grounds. Then he asked her also what he had best to do further to them. So she asked him what they were, whence they came, and whither they were bound; and he told her. Then she counselled him that when he arose in the morning he should beat them without any mercy. So, when he arose, he getteth him a grievous crab-tree cudgel, and goes down into the dungeon to them, and there first falls to rating of them as if they were dogs, although they never gave him a word of distaste. Then he falls upon them, and beats them fearfully, in such sort, that they were not able to help themselves, or to turn them upon

the floor. This done, he withdraws and leaves them, there to condole their misery, and to mourn under their distress. So all that day they spent the time in nothing but sighs and bitter lamentations. The next night, she, talking with her husband about them further, and understanding they were yet alive, did advise him to counsel them to make away with themselves. So when morning was come, he goes to them in a surly manner as before, and perceiving them to be very sore with the stripes that he had given them the day before, he told them, that since they were never like to come out of that place, their only way would be forthwith to make an end of themselves, either with knife, halter, or poison, for why, said he, should you choose life, seeing it is attended with so much bitterness? But they desired him to let them go. With that he looked ugly upon them, and, rushing to them, had doubtless made an end of them himself, but that he fell into one of his fits (for he sometimes, in sunshiny weather, fell into fits), and lost for a time the use of his hand; wherefore he withdrew, and left them as before, to consider what to do. Then did the prisoners consult between themselves, whether it was best to take his counsel or no; and thus they began to discourse:

Chr. Brother, said Christian, what shall we do? The life that we now live is miserable. For

my part I know not whether it is best, to live thus, or to die out of hand. "My soul chooseth strangling rather than life," and the grave is more easy for me than this dungeon. Shall we be ruled by the Giant?

Hope. Indeed, our present condition is dreadful, and death would be far more welcome to me than thus for ever to abide; but yet, let us consider, the Lord of the country to which we are going hath said, Thou shalt do no murder: no, not to another man's person; much more, then, are we forbidden to take his counsel to kill ourselves. Besides, he that kills another, can but commit murder upon his body; but for one to kill himself is to kill body and soul at once. And let us consider, again, that all the law is not in the hand of Giant Despair. Others, so far as I can understand, have been taken by him, as well as we; and yet have escaped out of his hand. Who knows, but that God that made the world may cause that Giant Despair may die? or that, at some time or other, he may forget to lock us in? or that he may, in a short time, have another of his fits before us, and may lose the use of his limbs? and if ever that should come to pass again, for my part, I am resolved to pluck up the heart of a man, and to try my utmost to get from under his hand. I was a fool that I did not try to do it before; but, however,

my brother, let us be patient, and endure a while. The time may come that may give us a happy release; but let us not be our own murderers. With these words, Hopeful at present did moderate the mind of his brother; so they continued together (in the dark) that day, in their sad and doleful condition.

Well, towards evening, the Giant goes down into the dungeon again, to see if his prisoners had taken his counsel; but when he came there he found them alive; and truly, alive was all; for now, what for want of bread and water, and by reason of the wounds they received when he beat them, they could do little but breathe. But, I say, he found them alive; at which he fell into a grievous rage, and told them that, seeing they had disobeyed his counsel, it should be worse with them than if they had never been born.

At this they trembled greatly, and I think that Christian fell into a swoon; but, coming a little to himself again, they renewed their discourse about the Giant's counsel; and whether yet they had best to take it or no. Now Christian again seemed to be for doing it, but Hopeful made his second reply as followeth:

Hope. My brother, said he, rememberest thou not how valiant thou hast been heretofore? Apollyon could not crush thee, nor could all that thou didst hear, or see, or feel, in the Valley

of the Shadow of Death. What hardship, terror, and amazement hast thou already gone through! And art thou now nothing but fear! Thou seest that I am in the dungeon with thee, a far weaker man by nature than thou art; also, this Giant hath wounded me as well as thee, and hath also cut off the bread and water from my mouth; and with thee I mourn without the light. But let us exercise a little more patience; remember how thou playedst the man at Vanity Fair, and wast neither afraid of the chain, nor cage, nor yet of bloody death. Wherefore let us (at least to avoid the shame, that becomes not a Christian to be found in) bear up with patience as well as we can.

Now, night being come again, and the Giant and his wife being in bed, she asked him concerning the prisoners, and if they had taken his counsel. To which he replied, They are sturdy rogues, they choose rather to bear all hardship, than to make away with themselves. Then said she, Take them into the castle-yard to-morrow, and show them the bones and skulls of those that thou hast already despatched, and make them believe, ere a week comes to an end, thou also wilt tear them in pieces, as thou hast done their fellows before them.

So when the morning was come, the Giant goes to them again, and takes them into the

castle-yard, and shows them, as his wife had bidden him. These, said he, were pilgrims as you are, once, and they trespassed in my grounds, as you have done; and when I thought fit, I tore them in pieces, and so, within ten days, I will do you. Go, get you down to your den again; and with that he beat them all the way thither. They lay, therefore, all day on Saturday in a lamentable case, as before. Now, when night was come, and when Mrs. Diffidence and her husband, the Giant, were got to bed, they began to renew their discourse of their prisoners; and withal the old Giant wondered, that he could neither by his blows nor his counsel bring them to an end. And with that his wife replied, I fear, said she, that they live in hope that some will come to relieve them, or that they have pick-locks about them, by the means of which they hope to escape. And sayest thou so, my dear? said the Giant; I will, therefore, search them in the morning.

Well, on Saturday, about midnight, they began to pray, and continued in prayer till almost break of day.

Now, a little before it was day, good Christian, as one half amazed, brake out in this passionate speech: What a fool, quoth he, am I, thus to lie in a stinking dungeon, when I may as well walk at liberty! I have a key in my bosom, called

Promise, that will, I am persuaded, open any lock in Doubting Castle. Then said Hopeful, That is good news, good brother; pluck it out of thy bosom, and try.

Then Christian pulled it out of his bosom, and began to try at the dungeon door, whose bolt (as he turned the key) gave back, and the door flew open with ease, and Christian and Hopeful both came out. Then he went to the outward door that leads into the castle-yard, and, with his key, opened that door also. After, he went to the iron gate, for that must be opened too; but that lock went very hard, yet the key did open it. Then they thrust open the gate to make their escape with speed, but that gate, as it opened, made such a creaking, that it waked Giant Despair, who, hastily rising to pursue his prisoners, felt his limbs to fail, for his fits took him again, so that he could by no means go after them. Then they went on, and came to the King's highway, and so were safe, because they were out of his jurisdiction.

Now, when they were gone over the stile, they began to contrive with themselves what they should do at that stile, to prevent those that should come after, from falling into the hands of Giant Despair. So they consented to erect there a pillar, and to engrave upon the side thereof this sentence—" Over this stile is the

way to Doubting Castle, which is kept by Giant Despair, who despiseth the King of the Celestial Country, and seeks to destroy his holy pilgrims." Many, therefore, that followed after, read what was written, and escaped the danger.

THE DELECTABLE MOUNTAINS

They went then till they came to the Delectable Mountains, which mountains belong to the Lord of that hill of which we have spoken before; so they went up to the mountains, to behold the gardens and orchards, the vineyards and fountains of water; where also they drank and washed themselves, and did freely eat of the vineyards. Now there were on the tops of these mountains shepherds feeding their flocks, and they stood by the highway side. The pilgrims therefore went to them, and leaning upon their staves (as is common with weary pilgrims, when they stand to talk with any by the way), they asked, Whose Delectable Mountains are these? And whose be the sheep that feed upon them?

Shep. These mountains are Immanuel's Land, and they are within sight of his city; and the sheep also are his, and he laid down his life for them.

Chr. Is this the way to the Celestial City?

Shep. You are just in your way.

Chr. How far is it thither?

Shep. Too far for any but those that shall get thither indeed.

Chr. Is the way safe or dangerous?

Shep. Safe for those for whom it is to be safe; " but the transgressors shall fall therein."

Chr. Is there, in this place, any relief for pilgrims that are weary and faint in the way?

Shep. The Lord of these mountains hath given us a charge not to be " forgetful to entertain strangers "; therefore the good of the place is before you.

I saw also in my dream, that when the Shepherds perceived that they were wayfaring men, they also put questions to them, to which they made answer as in other places; as, Whence came you? and, How got you into the way? and, By what means have you so persevered? For but few of them that begin to come hither, do show their face on these mountains. But when the Shepherds heard their answers, being pleased therewith, they looked very lovingly upon them, and said, Welcome to the Delectable Mountains. The Shepherds, I say, whose names were Knowledge, Experience, Watchful, and Sincere, took them by the hand, and had them to their tents, and made them partake of that which was ready at present. They said, moreover, We would that ye should stay here awhile, to be acquainted

with us; and yet more to solace yourselves with the good of these Delectable Mountains. They then told them, that they were content to stay; so they went to their rest that night, because it was very late.

Then I saw in my dream, that in the morning the Shepherds called up Christian and Hopeful to walk with them upon the mountains; so they went forth with them, and walked a while, having a pleasant prospect on every side. Then said the Shepherds one to another, Shall we show these pilgrims some wonders? So when they had concluded to do it, they had them first to the top of a hill called Error, which was very steep on the furthest side, and bid them look down to the bottom. So Christian and Hopeful looked down, and saw at the bottom several men dashed all to pieces by a fall that they had from the top.

Then I saw that they had them to the top of another mountain, and the name of that is Caution, and bid them look afar off; which, when they did, they perceived, as they thought, several men walking up and down among the tombs that were there; and they perceived that the men were blind, because they stumbled sometimes upon the tombs, and because they could not get out from among them. Then said Christian, What means this?

The Shepherds then answered, Did you not

see a little below these mountains a stile, that led into a meadow, on the left hand of this way? They answered, Yes. Then said the Shepherds, From that stile there goes a path that leads directly to Doubting Castle, which is kept by Giant Despair, and these, pointing to them among the tombs, came once on pilgrimage, as you do now, even till they came to that same stile; and because the right way was rough in that place, they chose to go out of it into that meadow, and there were taken by Giant Despair, and cast into Doubting Castle; where, after they had been a while kept in the dungeon, he at last did put out their eyes, and led them among those tombs, where he has left them to wander to this very day, that the saying of the wise man might be fulfilled, " He that wandereth out of the way of understanding, shall remain in the congregation of the dead." Then Christian and Hopeful looked upon one another, with tears gushing out, but yet said nothing to the Shepherds.

By this time the pilgrims had a desire to go forward, and the Shepherds a desire they should; so they walked together towards the end of the mountains. Then said the Shepherds one to another, Let us here show to the pilgrims the gates of the Celestial City, if they have skill to look through our perspective glass. The pilgrims then lovingly accepted the motion; so they had

them to the top of a high hill, called Clear, and gave them their glass to look.

Then they essayed to look, and they thought they saw something like the gate, and also some of the glory of the place. Then they went away.

When they were about to depart, one of the Shepherds gave them a note of the way. Another of them bid them beware of the Flatterer. The third bid them take heed that they sleep not upon the Enchanted Ground. And the fourth bid them God-speed. So I woke from my dream.

IGNORANCE

And I slept, and dreamed again, and saw the same two pilgrims going down the mountains along the highway towards the city. Now, a little below these mountains, on the left hand, lieth the country of Conceit; from which country there comes into the way in which the pilgrims walked, a little crooked lane. Here, therefore, they met with a very brisk lad, that came out of that country; and his name was Ignorance. So Christian asked him from what parts he came, and whither he was going.

Ignor. Sir, I was born in the country that

So I woke, etc. Perhaps Bunyan means by this break in the story to tell us of his release from prison (1676). The book was probably finished immediately he was free.

lieth off there a little on the left hand, and I am going to the Celestial City.

Chr. But how do you think to get in at the gate? for you may find some difficulty there.

Ignor. As other good people do, said he.

Chr. But what have you to show at that gate, that may cause that the gate should be opened to you?

Ignor. I know my Lord's will, and I have been a good liver; I pay every man his own; I pray, fast, pay tithes, and give alms, and have left my country for whither I am going.

Chr. But thou camest not in at the wicket-gate that is at the head of this way; thou camest in hither through that same crooked lane, and therefore, I fear, however thou mayest think of thyself, when the reckoning day shall come, thou wilt have laid to thy charge that thou art a thief and a robber, instead of getting admittance into the city.

Ignor. Gentlemen, ye be utter strangers to me, I know you not; be content to follow the religion of your country, and I will follow the religion of mine. I hope all will be well. And as for the gate that you talk of, all the world knows that that is a great way off of our country. I cannot think that any man in all our parts doth so much as know the way to it, nor need they matter whether they do or no, since we have, as you

see, a fine, pleasant green lane, that comes down from our country, the next way into the way.

When Christian saw that the man was " wise in his own conceit," he said to Hopeful whisperingly, " There is more hope of a fool than of him."

THE STORY OF LITTLE-FAITH

So they both went on, and Ignorance he came after. Now when they had passed him a little way, they entered into a very dark lane. Then said Christian to his fellow, Now I call to remembrance, that which was told me of a thing that happened to a good man hereabout. The name of the man was Little-faith, but a good man, and he dwelt in the town of Sincere. The thing was this: At the entering in at this passage, there comes down from Broad-way Gate, a lane called Dead Man's Lane; so called because of the murders that are commonly done there; and this Little-faith going on pilgrimage, as we do now, chanced to sit down there, and slept. Now there happened, at that time, to come down the lane, from Broad-way Gate, three sturdy rogues, and their names were Faint-heart, Mistrust, and Guilt (three brothers), and they espying Little-faith, where he was, came galloping up with speed. Now the good man was just

awake from his sleep, and was getting up to go
on his journey. So they came up all to him, and
with threatening language bid him stand. At
this Little-faith looked as white as a clout, and
had neither power to fight nor fly. Then said
Faint-heart, Deliver thy purse. But he making
no haste to do it (for he was loth to lose his
money), Mistrust ran up to him, and thrusting
his hand into his pocket, pulled out thence a
bag of silver. Then he cried out, Thieves!
Thieves! With that Guilt, with a great club
that was in his hand, struck Little-faith on the
head, and with that blow, felled him flat to the
ground, where he lay bleeding as one that would
bleed to death. All this while the thieves stood
by. But, at last, they hearing that some were
on the road, and fearing lest it should be one
Great-grace, that dwells in the city of Good-
confidence, they betook themselves to their
heels, and left this good man to shift for himself.
Now, after a while, Little-faith came to himself,
and getting up, made shift to scrabble on his
way. This was the story.

Hope. But did they take from him all that
ever he had?

Chr. No; the place where his jewels were
they never ransacked, so those he kept still. But,
as I was told, the good man was much afflicted
for his loss, for the thieves got most of his

F

spending-money. That which they got not (as I said) were jewels, also he had a little odd money left, but scarce enough to bring him to his journey's end; nay, if I was not misinformed, he was forced to beg as he went, to keep himself alive; for his jewels he might not sell. But beg, and do what he could, he went (as we say) with many a hungry belly, the most part of the rest of the way.

Hope. But is it not a wonder they got not from him his certificate, by which he was to receive his admittance at the Celestial Gate?

Chr. It is a wonder; but they got not that, though they missed it not through any good cunning of his; for he, being dismayed with their coming upon him, had neither power nor skill to hide anything; so it was more by good Providence than by his endeavour, that they missed of that good thing.

Hope. But it must needs be a comfort to him, that they got not his jewels from him.

Chr. It might have been great comfort to him, had he used it as he should; but they that told me the story said, that he made but little use of it all the rest of the way, and that because of the dismay that he had in the taking away his money; indeed, he forgot it a great part of the rest of his journey; and besides, when at any

Spending-money. Money for the journey.

time it came into his mind, and he began to be comforted therewith, then would fresh thoughts of his loss come again upon him, and those thoughts would swallow up all.

Hope. Alas! poor man. This could not but be a great grief to him.

Chr. Grief! ay, a grief indeed. Would it not have been so to any of us, had we been used as he, to be robbed, and wounded too, and that in a strange place, as he was? It is a wonder he did not die with grief, poor heart! I was told that he scattered almost all the rest of the way with nothing but doleful and bitter complaints; telling also to all that overtook him, or that he overtook in the way as he went, where he was robbed, and how; who they were that did it, and what he lost; how he was wounded, and that he hardly escaped with his life.

Hope. But it is a wonder that his necessity did not put him upon selling or pawning some of his jewels, that he might have wherewith to relieve himself in his journey.

Chr. Thou talkest like one upon whose head is the shell to this very day; for what should he pawn them, or to whom should he sell them? In all that country where he was robbed, his jewels were not accounted of; nor did he want

---

Thou talkest like one, etc. Like a mere chick just hatched, that is with no sense at all.

that relief which could from thence be administered to him. Besides, had his jewels been missing at the gate of the Celestial City, he had (and that he knew well enough) been excluded from an inheritance there; and that would have been worse to him than the appearance and villainy of ten thousand thieves.

But, consider again, they are but journeymen thieves, they serve under the king of the bottomless pit, who, if need be, will come in to their aid himself, and his voice is as the roaring of a lion. I myself have been engaged as this Littlefaith was, and I found it a terrible thing. These three villains set upon me, and I beginning, like a Christian, to resist, they gave but a call, and in came their master. I would, as the saying is, have given my life for a penny; but that, as God would have it, I was clothed with armour of proof. Ay, and yet, though I was so harnessed, I found it hard work to quit myself like a man. No man can tell what in that combat attends us, but he that hath been in the battle himself.

Hope. Well, but they ran, you see, when they did but suppose that one Great-grace was in the way.

Chr. True, they have often fled, both they

Journeymen thieves. Of no account. A journeyman was a man who worked by the day (French *journée*) and went from master to master. He was not considered a first-class workman.

and their master, when Great-grace hath but appeared; and no marvel; for he is the King's champion. But, I trow, you will put some difference betwixt Little-faith and the King's champion. All the King's subjects are not his champions, nor can they, when tried, do such feats of war as he. Is it meet to think that a little child should handle Goliath as David did? Or that there should be the strength of an ox in a wren? Some are strong, some are weak; some have great faith, some have little. This man was one of the weak, and therefore he went to the wall.

Hope. I would it had been Great-grace for their sakes.

Chr. If it had been, he might have had his hands full; for I must tell you, that though Great-grace is excellent good at his weapons, and has, and can, so long as he keeps them at sword's point, do well enough with them; yet, if they get within him, even Faint-heart, Mistrust, or the other, it shall go hard but they will throw up his heels. And when a man is down, you know, what can he do?

Whoso looks well upon Great-grace's face, shall see those scars and cuts there, that shall easily give demonstration of what I say. Yea, once I heard that he should say (and that when he was in the combat), " We despaired even of life."

But for such footmen as thou and I are, let us never desire to meet with an enemy, nor vaunt as if we could do better, when we hear of others that they have been foiled, nor be tickled at the thoughts of our own manhood; for such commonly come by the worst when tried. Witness Peter, of whom I made mention before. He would swagger, ay, he would; he would, as his vain mind prompted him to say, do better, and stand more for his Master than all men; but who so foiled, and run down by these villains, as he?

When, therefore, we hear that such robberies are done on the King's highway, two things become us to do: 1. To go out harnessed, and to be sure to take a shield with us; for it was for want of that, that he that laid so lustily at Leviathan could not make him yield: for, indeed, if that be wanting, he fears us not at all. Therefore, he that had skill hath said, " Above all, taking the shield of faith, wherewith ye shall be able to quench all the fiery darts of the wicked."

2. It is good, also, that we desire of the King a convoy yea, that he will go with us himself. This made David rejoice when in the Valley of the Shadow of Death; and Moses was rather for dying where he stood, than to go one step without his God. Oh, my brother, if he will but

Footmen. Mere infantrymen, just ordinary soldiers.

go along with us, what need we be afraid of ten thousands that shall set themselves against us? But, without him, the proud helpers "fall under the slain."

I, for my part, have been in the fray before now; and though, through the goodness of him that is best, I am, as you see, alive; yet I cannot boast of my manhood. Glad shall I be, if I meet with no more such brunts; though I fear we are not got beyond all danger. However, since the lion and the bear have not as yet devoured me, I hope God will also deliver us from the next uncircumcised Philistine.

THE PILGRIMS IN THE NET

They went then till they came at a place where they saw a way put itself into their way, and seemed withal to lie as straight as the way which they should go: and here they knew not which of the two to take, for both seemed straight before them; therefore, here they stood still to consider. And as they were thinking about the way, behold a man, black of flesh, but covered with a very light robe, came to them, and asked them why they stood there. They answered they were going to the Celestial City, but knew not which of these ways to take. Follow me, said the man, it is thither that I am going. So

they followed him in the way that but now came into the road, which by degrees turned, and turned them so from the city that they desired to go to, that, in little time, their faces were turned away from it; yet they followed him. But by and by, before they were aware, he led them both within the compass of a net, in which they were both so entangled, that they knew not what to do; and with that the white robe fell off the black man's back. Then they saw where they were. Wherefore, there they lay crying some time, for they could not get themselves out.

Chr. Then said Christian to his fellow, Now do I see myself in error. Did not the Shepherds bid us beware of the flatterers? As is the saying of the wise man, so we have found it this day, " A man that flattereth his neighbour, spreadeth a net for his feet."

Hope. They also gave us a note of directions about the way, for our more sure finding thereof; but therein we have also forgotten to read, and have not kept ourselves from the paths of the destroyer. Here David was wiser than we; for, saith he, " Concerning the works of men, by the word of thy lips, I have kept me from the paths of the destroyer." Thus they lay bewailing themselves in the net. At last they espied a Shining One coming towards them with a whip of small cord in his hand. When he was come to

the place where they were, he asked them whence they came, and what they did there. They told him that they were poor pilgrims going to Zion, but were led out of their way by a black man, clothed in white, who bid us, said they, follow him, for he was going thither too. Then said he with the whip, It is Flatterer, a false apostle, that hath transformed himself into an angel of light. So he rent the net, and let the men out. Then said he to them, Follow me, that I may set you in your way again. So he led them back to the way which they had left to follow the Flatterer. Then he asked them, saying, Where did you lie the last night? They said, With the Shepherds upon the Delectable Mountains. He asked them then, if they had not of those Shepherds a note of direction for the way. They answered, Yes. But did you, said he, when you were at a stand, pluck out and read your note? They answered, No. He asked them, Why? They said, They forgot. He asked, moreover, if the Shepherds did not bid them beware of the Flatterer. They answered, Yes, but we did not imagine, said they, that this fine-spoken man had been he.

Then I saw in my dream, that he commanded them to lie down; which, when they did, he chastised them sore, to teach them the good way wherein they should walk; and as he chastised

*F

them he said, "As many as I love, I rebuke and chasten; be zealous, therefore, and repent." This done, he bid them go on their way, and take good heed to the other directions of the Shepherds. So they thanked him for all his kindness, and went softly along the right way.

THE ENCHANTED GROUND

I saw then in my dream, that they went till they came into a certain country, whose air naturally tended to make one drowsy, if he came a stranger into it. And here Hopeful began to be very dull and heavy of sleep; wherefore he said unto Christian, I do now begin to grow so drowsy that I can scarcely hold up mine eyes; let us lie down here and take one nap.

Chr. By no means, said the other; lest sleeping, we never awake more.

Hope. Why, my brother? Sleep is sweet to the labouring man; we may be refreshed if we take a nap.

Chr. Do you not remember that one of the Shepherds bid us beware of the Enchanted Ground? He meant by that, that we should beware of sleeping; "Therefore let us not sleep, as do others, but let us watch and be sober."

Hope. I acknowledge myself in a fault; and had I been here alone, I had by sleeping run the

danger of death. I see it is true that the wise man saith, " Two are better than one." Hitherto hath thy company been my mercy, and thou shalt have a good reward for thy labour.

THE COUNTRY OF BEULAH

Now I saw in my dream, that by this time the pilgrims were got over the Enchanted Ground, and entering into the country of Beulah, whose air was very sweet and pleasant, the way lying directly through it, they solaced themselves there for a season. Yea, here they heard continually the singing of birds, and saw every day the flowers appear in the earth, and heard the voice of the turtle in the land. In this country the sun shineth night and day; wherefore this was beyond the Valley of the Shadow of Death, and also out of the reach of Giant Despair, neither could they from this place so much as see Doubting Castle. Here they were within sight of the city they were going to, also here met them some of the inhabitants thereof; for in this land the Shining Ones commonly walked, because it was upon the borders of heaven. In this land also, the contract between the bride and the bridegroom was renewed; yea, here, " As the bridegroom rejoiceth over the bride, so did their God rejoice over them." Here they

had no want of corn and wine; for in this place they met with abundance of what they had sought for in all their pilgrimage. Here they heard voices from out of the city, loud voices, saying, "Say ye to the daughter of Zion, Behold, thy salvation cometh! Behold, his reward is with him!" Here all the inhabitants of the country called them, "The holy people, The redeemed of the Lord, Sought out."

Now, as they walked in this land, they had more rejoicing than in parts more remote from the kingdom to which they were bound; and drawing near to the city, they had yet a more perfect view thereof. It was builded of pearls and precious stones, also the street thereof was paved with gold; so that by reason of the natural glory of the city, and the reflection of the sun-beams upon it, Christian with desire fell sick; Hopeful also had a fit or two of the same disease.

But, being a little strengthened, and better able to bear their sickness, they walked on their way, and came yet nearer and nearer, where were orchards, vineyards, and gardens, and their gates opened into the highway. Now, as they came up to these places, behold the gardener stood in the way, to whom the pilgrims said, Whose goodly vineyards and gardens are these? He answered, They are the King's, and are planted here for his own delight, and also for

the solace of pilgrims. So the gardener had them into the vineyards, and bid them refresh themselves with the dainties. He also showed them there the King's walks, and the arbours where he delighted to be; and here they tarried and slept.

Now I beheld in my dream, that they talked more in their sleep at this time than ever they did in all their journey; and being in a muse thereabout, the gardener said even to me, Wherefore musest thou at the matter? It is the nature of the fruit of the grapes of these vineyards to go down so sweetly as to cause the lips of them that are asleep to speak.

So I saw that when they awoke, they addressed themselves to go up to the city; but, as I said, the reflection of the sun upon the city (for " the city was pure gold ") was so extremely glorious, that they could not, as yet, with open face behold it, but through an instrument made for that purpose. So I saw, that as I went on, there met them two men, in raiment that shone like gold; also their faces shone as the light.

These men asked the pilgrims whence they came; and they told them. They also asked them where they had lodged, what difficulties and dangers, what comforts and pleasures they had met in the way; and they told them. Then said the men that met them, You have but two

difficulties more to meet with, and then you are in the city.

Christian then, and his companion, asked the men to go along with them; so they told them they would. But, said they, you must obtain it by your own faith.

CROSSING THE RIVER

So I saw in my dream that they went on together, until they came in sight of the gate.

Now, I further saw, that betwixt them and the gate was a river, but there was no bridge to go over: the river was very deep. At the sight, therefore, of this river, the pilgrims were much stunned; but the men that went with them said, You must go through, or you cannot come at the gate.

The pilgrims then began to inquire if there was no other way to the gate; to which they answered, Yes; but there hath not any, save two, to wit, Enoch and Elijah, been permitted to tread that path, since the foundation of the world, nor shall, until the last trumpet shall sound. The pilgrims then, especially Christian, began to despond in their minds, and looked this way and that, but no way could be found by them, by which they might escape the river. Then they asked the men if the waters were all

THE PASSAGE OF THE RIVER OF DEATH

THE PASSAGE OF THE RIVER OF DEATH

of a depth. They said, No; yet they could not help them in that case; for, said they, you shall find it deeper or shallower, as you believe in the King of the place.

They then addressed themselves to the water; and entering, Christian began to sink, and crying out to his good friend Hopeful, he said, I sink in deep waters; the billows go over my head, all his waves go over me!

Then said the other, Be of good cheer, my brother, I feel the bottom, and it is good. Then said Christian, Ah! my friend, " the sorrows of death have compassed me about "; I shall not see the land that flows with milk and honey; and with that a great darkness and horror fell upon Christian, so that he could not see before him. Also here he in great measure lost his senses, so that he could neither remember, nor orderly talk of any of those sweet refreshments that he had met with in the way of his pilgrimage. But all the words that he spake still tended to discover that he had horror of mind, and heart fears that he should die in that river, and never obtain entrance in at the gate. Here also, as they that stood by perceived, he was much in the troublesome thoughts of the sins that he had committed, both since and before he began to be a pilgrim. It was also observed that he was troubled with apparitions of hobgoblins and

evil spirits, for ever and anon he would intimate
so much by words. Hopeful, therefore, here had
much ado to keep his brother's head above
water; yea, sometimes he would be quite gone
down, and then, ere a while, he would rise up
again half dead. Hopeful also would endeavour
to comfort him, saying, Brother, I see the gate,
and men standing by to receive us; but Christian
would answer, It is you, it is you they wait for;
you have been Hopeful ever since I knew you.
And so have you, said he to Christian. Ah,
brother! said he, surely if I was right he would
now arise to help me; but for my sins he hath
brought me into the snare, and hath left me.
Then said Hopeful, These troubles and distresses
that you go through in these waters are no sign
that God hath forsaken you; but are sent to
try you, whether you will call to mind that which
heretofore you have received of his goodness, and
live upon him in your distresses.

Then I saw in my dream, that Christian was
as in a muse a while. To whom also Hopeful
added this word, Be of good cheer. Jesus Christ
maketh thee whole; and with that Christian
brake out with a loud voice, Oh! I see him again,
and he tells me, "When thou passest through
the waters, I will be with thee; and through
the rivers, they shall not overflow thee." Then
they both took courage, and the enemy was after

that as still as a stone, until they were gone over. Christian therefore presently found ground to stand upon, and so it followed that the rest of the river was but shallow. Thus they got over.

THE APPROACH TO THE CITY

Now, upon the bank of the river, on the other side, they saw the two shining men again, who there waited for them; wherefore, being come out of the river, they saluted them saying, We are ministering spirits, sent forth to minister for those that shall be heirs of salvation. Thus they went along towards the gate.

Now you must note that the city stood upon a mighty hill, but the pilgrims went up that hill with ease, because they had these two men to lead them up by the arms; also, they had left their mortal garments behind them in the river, for though they went in with them, they came out without them. They, therefore, went up here with much agility and speed, though the foundation upon which the city was framed was higher than the clouds. They, therefore, went up through the regions of the air, sweetly talking as they went, being comforted, because they safely got over the river, and had such glorious companions to attend them.

The talk they had with the Shining Ones was

about the glory of the place; who told them that the beauty and glory of it was inexpressible. There, said they, is the "Mount Zion, the heavenly Jerusalem, the innumerable company of angels, and the spirits of just men made perfect." You are going now, said they, to the paradise of God, wherein you shall see the tree of life, and eat of the never-fading fruits thereof; and when you come there, you shall have white robes given you, and your walk and talk shall be every day with the King, even all the days of eternity. There you shall not see again such things as you saw when you were in the lower region upon the earth, to wit, sorrow, sickness, affliction, and death, "for the former things are passed away." You are now going to Abraham, to Isaac, and Jacob, and to the prophets—men that God hath taken away from the evil to come, and that are now resting upon their beds, each one walking in his righteousness. The men then asked, What must we do in the holy place? To whom it was answered, You must there receive the comforts of all your toil, and have joy for all your sorrow; you must reap what you have sown, even the fruit of all your prayers, and tears, and sufferings for the King by the way. In that place you must wear crowns of gold, and enjoy the perpetual sight and vision of the Holy One, for "there you shall see him

as he is." There also you shall serve him continually with praise, with shouting, and thanksgiving, whom you desired to serve in the world, though with much difficulty, because of the infirmity of your flesh. There your eyes shall be delighted with seeing, and your ears with hearing the pleasant voice of the Mighty One. There you shall enjoy your friends again, that are gone thither before you; and there you shall with joy receive, even every one that follows into the holy place after you. There also shall you be clothed with glory and majesty, and put into an equipage fit to ride out with the King of glory.

THE CELESTIAL CITY

Now while they were thus drawing towards the gate, behold a company of the heavenly host came out to meet them; to whom it was said, by the other two Shining Ones, These are the men that have loved our Lord when they were in the world, and that have left all for his holy name; and he hath sent us to fetch them, and we have brought them thus far on their desired journey, that they may go in and look their Redeemer in the face with joy. Then the heavenly host gave a great shout, saying, "Blessed are they which are called unto the marriage supper of the Lamb." There came out also at this time

to meet them, several of the King's trumpeters, clothed in white and shining raiment, who, with melodious noises, and loud, made even the heavens to echo with their sound. These trumpeters saluted Christian and his fellow with ten thousand welcomes from the world; and this they did with shouting, and sound of trumpet.

This done, they compassed them round on every side; some went before, some behind, and some on the right hand, some on the left (as it were to guard them through the upper regions), continually sounding as they went, with melodious noise, in notes on high: so that the very sight was to them that could behold it, as if heaven itself was come down to meet them. Thus, therefore, they walked on together; and as they walked, ever and anon these trumpeters, even with joyful sound, would, by mixing their music with looks and gestures, still signify to Christian and his brother, how welcome they were into their company, and with what gladness they came to meet them; and now were these two men, as it were, in heaven, before they came at it, being swallowed up with the sight of angels, and with hearing of their melodious notes. Here also they had the city itself in view, and they thought they heard all the bells therein to ring, to welcome them thereto. But above all, the warm and joyful thoughts that they had about

their own dwelling there, with such company, and that for ever and ever! Oh, by what tongue or pen can their glorious joy be expressed! And thus they came up to the gate.

Now, when they were come up to the gate, there was written over it in letters of gold, " Blessed are they that do his commandments, that they may have right to the tree of life, and may enter in through the gates into the city."

Then I saw in my dream, that the Shining Men bid them call at the gate; the which, when they did, some looked from above over the gate, to wit, Enoch, Moses, and Elijah, etc., to whom it was said, These pilgrims are come from the City of Destruction, for the love that they bear to the King of this place; and then the pilgrims gave in unto them each man his certificate, which they had received in the beginning; those, therefore, were carried in to the King, who, when he had read them, said, Where are the men? To whom it was answered, They are standing without the gate. The King then commanded to open the gate, " That the righteous nation," said he, " which keepeth the truth, may enter in."

Now I saw in my dream that these two men went in at the gate: and lo, as they entered, they were transfigured, and they had raiment put on that shone like gold. There were also

that met them with harps and crowns, and gave them to them—the harps to praise withal, and the crowns in token of honour. Then I heard in my dream that all the bells in the city rang again for joy, and that it was said unto them, "ENTER YE INTO THE JOY OF YOUR LORD." I also heard the men themselves, that they sang with a loud voice, saying, "BLESSING AND HONOUR, AND GLORY, AND POWER, BE UNTO HIM THAT SITTETH UPON THE THRONE, AND UNTO THE LAMB, FOR EVER AND EVER."

Now, just as the gates were opened to let in the men, I looked in after them, and, behold, the City shone like the sun; the streets also were paved with gold, and in them walked many men, with crowns on their heads, palms in their hands, and golden harps to sing praises withal.

There were also of them that had wings, and they answered one another without intermission, saying, "Holy, holy, holy is the Lord." And after that they shut up the gates; which, when I had seen, I wished myself among them.

DRAMATISED VERSION

ARRANGED BY

N. T. CARRINGTON, M.A.

PART I

CHARACTERS

CHRISTIAN.
EVANGELIST.

PORTER OF THE HOUSE BEAUTIFUL.
LADY OF THE HOUSE BEAUTIFUL.

APOLLYON.

FAITHFUL.
JUDGE HATEGOOD.
CLERK.
ENVY
SUPERSTITION } *witnesses.*
PICKTHANK
MR. BLIND-MAN (*foreman*)
MR. NO-GOOD
MR. MALICE
MR. LOVE-LUST
MR. LIVE-LOOSE
MR. HEADY
MR. HIGH-MIND } *jurymen.*
MR. ENMITY
MR. LYAR
MR. CRUELTY
MR. HATE-LIGHT
MR. IMPLACABLE
CITIZENS, GAOLERS, ETC.

HOPEFUL.

GIANT DESPAIR.
HIS WIFE.

TWO SHEPHERDS.

TWO MEN FROM THE CITY OF ZION.
GATEKEEPER OF THE CITY OF ZION.

PART I

ACT I

Scene I

Common outside the City of Destruction.

Enter Christian (clothed in rags, an old Bible in his hand, and a great burden on his back), looking this way and that, his hands shading his eyes. Suddenly keeps his eyes fixed in one direction. From this direction enter Evangelist.

Evangelist.   Why standest thou still?

Christian.   Because I know not whither to go.
      [*Evangelist gives him a parchment roll.*

Chr. [*Reading from the roll.*]   "Fly from the wrath to come." [*Slowly and thoughtfully, looking up at Evan.*]   Whither must I fly?

Evan. [*Pointing.*]   Do you see yonder Wicket Gate?

Chr. [*After a moment's pause.*]   No.

Evan.   Do you see yonder shining light?

Chr. [*Slowly and with hesitation.*]   I think I do.

Evan.   Keep that light in your eye, and go up directly thereto, so shalt thou see the Gate; at

which when thou knockest, it shall be told thee what thou shalt do. Thereafter thou shalt lose thy burden, and be clothed with a change of raiment. But how is it that thou camest alone from the City of Destruction?

Chr. Because none of my neighbours saw their danger as I saw mine.

Evan. Did any of them know of your coming?

Chr. Yes, my wife and children saw me at the first, and called after me to turn again: also some of my neighbours stood crying, and calling after me to return, but I put my fingers in my ears, and so came on my way.

Evan. But did none of them follow you to persuade you to go back?

Chr. Yes, both Obstinate and Pliable; but when they saw that they could not prevail, Obstinate went railing back, but Pliable came with me a little way.

Evan. But why did he not come through?

Chr. We indeed came both together, until we came at the Slough of Despond, into the which we also suddenly fell. And then was my neighbour Pliable discouraged, and would not adventure further. Wherefore getting out again on that side next to his own house, he told me I should possess the brave country alone for him. So he went his way, and I came mine; he after Obstinate, and I hither.

Evan. Alas, poor man! Is the celestial glory
  of so small esteem with him, that he counteth
  it not worth running the hazards of a few
  difficulties to obtain it? Christian! Turn not
  after Pliable. Look before you. That is your
  way, and God speed you.
Chr. I thank you, sir. Farewell!
        [*Exit running, Evangelist looking after him.*

CURTAIN

SCENE II

Entrance Hall of the House Beautiful.

*Time : evening. Lamp in the hall. Porter dozing
  on a chair near the door. A knock on the door is
  heard. Porter rubs his eyes, drowsily gets up,
  and opens the door. Christian, now well dressed
  and without his burden, is seen without, and as
  he is speaking, he gradually edges farther and
  farther over the threshold until he is in the hall.*

Chr. Sir, what house is this?
Porter. [*Sleepily.*] This house was built by the
  Lord of the Hill for the relief and security of
  pilgrims. But whence are you, and whither
  are you going?

Chr. I am come from the City of Destruction, and am going to Mount Zion, but because the sun is now set, I desire, if I may, to lodge here to-night.

Porter. What is your name?

Chr. My name is Christian.

Porter. But how doth it happen that you come so late?—the sun is set.

Chr. I had been here sooner, but that—wretched man that I am—I slept in the arbour that stands on the hill-side, and in my sleep I lost my parchment roll, and came without it to the brow of the hill, and then feeling for it and finding it not, I was forced to go back to the place where I slept, where I found it, and now I am come. I thank God I am here, for I found it hard work up the hill.

Porter. Well, I will call the lady of this place, who will, if she likes you, receive you into the house.   [*Exit.*

Chr. [*Looking round the hall.*] Where am I now? Is this the love and care of Jesus, thus to provide for pilgrims? Already it seems I dwell near heaven.

Enter Lady, followed by Porter.

Lady. Come, good Christian. We will receive you into our house this night, and let us talk with you of all things that have happened to

you in your pilgrimage; and in the morning
we will accompany you down to the foot of
the hill, for as it is difficult coming up, so it
is dangerous going down, yea, and though you
go very warily, yet I warrant you'll catch a
slip or two.   And ere you go forward you shall
be harnessed in proof mail, lest you meet with
assaults in the way.   But come now, the supper
is waiting.

> [*Exeunt Lady and Christian, Christian
> as he goes saluting the Porter farewell.*

CURTAIN

SCENE III

Valley of Humiliation.

*Enter Christian in breastplate, with a shield and
     sword.   He is frightened, now running back,
     now standing still, now running forward.*

Chr.   Would I were back in the House Beautiful.
What shall I do? [*Determinedly.*] I will stand.
—To flee would be to die, for my back is
unprotected, and had I no more in mine eye
than the saving of my life, 'twould be best
to stand.

Enter from opposite side Apollyon.

Apollyon. [*Disdainfully.*] Whence come you, and whither are you bound?

Chr. I am come from the City of Destruction, which is the place of all evil, and am going to the City of Zion.

Apol. By this I perceive thou art one of my subjects, for all that country is mine, and I am the Prince of it. How is it then that thou hast run away from thy King? Were it not that I hope thou mayest do me more service, I would strike thee now at one blow to the ground.

Chr. I was indeed born in your dominions, but your service was hard, and your wages such as a man could not live on, therefore when I was come to years, I did as other considerate persons do, look out if perhaps I might mend myself.

Apol. There is no Prince that will thus lightly lose his subjects, neither will I, as yet, lose thee. But since thou complainest of thy service and wages, be content to go back; what our country will afford, I do here promise to give thee.

Chr. But I have let myself to another, even to the King of Princes, and how can I with fairness go back with thee?

Apol. Thou hast done in this, according to the

proverb, changed a bad for a worse, but it is ordinary for those that have professed themselves his servants, after a while to give him the slip, and return again to me. Do thou so too, and all shall be well.

Chr. I have given him my faith, and sworn my allegiance to him, how then can I go back from this, and not be hanged as a traitor?

Apol. Thou didst the same to me, and yet I am willing to pass by all, if now thou wilt yet turn again, and go back.

Chr. What I promised thee was in my nonage, and besides, I count that the Prince, under whose banner now I stand, is able to pardon what I did as to my compliance with thee; and besides, to speak truth, I like his service, his wages, his servants, his government, his company, and country better than thine, and therefore leave off to persuade me further, I am his servant, and I will follow him.

Apol. Consider again when thou art in cool blood, what thou art like to meet with in the way that thou goest. Thou knowest that for the most part, his servants come to an ill end, because they are transgressors against me, and my ways. How many of them have been put to shameful deaths! And besides, thou countest his service better than mine, whereas he never came yet from the place where he is, to deliver

G

out of our hands any that served him; but as for me, how many times, as all the world very well knows, have I delivered, either by power or fraud, those that have faithfully served me, from him and his, and so I will deliver thee.

Chr. His forbearing at present to deliver them, is on purpose to try their love, whether they will cleave to him to the end, and as for the ill end thou sayest they come to, that is most glorious in their account. For, for present deliverance, they do not much expect it, for they stay for their glory, and then they shall have it, when their Prince comes in his.

Apol. Thou hast already been unfaithful in thy service to him, and how dost thou think to receive wages of him?

Chr. Wherein, O Apollyon, have I been unfaithful to him?

Apol. Thou didst faint at first setting out, when thou wast almost choked in the Gulf of Despond; thou didst attempt wrong ways to be rid of thy burden; thou didst sinfully sleep and lose thy choice thing; thou wast also almost persuaded to go back at the sight of lions; and when thou talkest of thy journey, and of what thou hast heard and seen, thou art inwardly desirous of vain-glory in all that thou sayest or doest.

Chr. All this is true, and much more, which

thou hast left out, but the Prince whom
I serve and honour is merciful and ready to
forgive. But besides, these infirmities possessed me in thy country, for there I sucked
them in, and I have groaned under them, been
sorry for them, and have obtained pardon of
my Prince.

Apol. [*Shouting in rage.*] I am an enemy to
this Prince. I hate his person, his laws,
and people. I am come out on purpose to
withstand thee.

Chr. Apollyon, beware what you do, for I am
in the king's highway, therefore take heed to
yourself.

Apol. [*Straddling over the path to prevent Christian's going on.*] I have no fear. Prepare
thyself to die, for I swear by my infernal den,
that thou shalt go no further. Here will
I spill thy soul.

[*Throws a dart at Christian, who wards it
off with his shield. Then rushes close to
Christian, wrestles with him, overthrows
him, and Christian's sword flies out of
his hand.*

[*Pressing on Christian's throat.*] I am sure of
thee now.

[*Draws back his right hand to give Christian a
final blow, but Christian nimbly reaches*

> *out his hand for his sword, gets it, gives*
> *him a thrust, which makes him give*
> *ground, follows it up with another, where-*
> *upon Apollyon runs off the stage howling,*
> *Christian after him.*

Chr. [*As he runs after Apollyon.*] Avaunt!
Avaunt, thou destroying Apollyon! [*Exeunt.*

CURTAIN

ACT II

SCENE: *Court of Law in Vanity Fair.*

Citizens are waiting for the court to open. Enter Faithful and Christian, looking dejected, in chains and irons, and guarded by two gaolers. Citizens whisper excitedly.

Faithful. I am glad that I overtook you, that we can come to danger as companions. I would rather cast in my lot with you than choose what is accounted wisest in this vain Fair.

First Citizen. For aught I can see, the men are quiet and sober, and intended nobody any harm.

Second Cit. [*Scratching his head in anger.*] I tell ye they're outlandish fools and bedlams, and were best be very roundly dealt withal.

First Cit. Nay, thou'rt a hot-spirited fellow. At most, three months in gaol will mend them.

Second Cit. Hot-spirited! Thou'rt a pestilent fellow, and art like to go the same way as these two babblers here. I tell ye plainly, they were best stretch by the neck for it, and what's more——

197

*Enter Judge, Court, and Attendants, etc. All stand
    until Judge is seated. The Clerk calls over
    the names of the Jurymen, and they answer.*

Judge. Read their indictment.
                        [*Nodding at Christian and Faithful.*
Clerk. That these men, Faithful and Christian,
    are enemies to and disturbers of the trade of
    our town, that they have devilishly and per-
    niciously made commotions in the streets, and
    have won a party to their own most dangerous
    opinions, in contempt of the law of our sovereign
    lord the king.
Faith. As for disturbance, I make none, being
    myself a man of peace. The parties that were
    won to us were won by beholding our truth and
    innocence, and they are turned only from the
    worse to the better. And as to the king you
    talk of, since he is Beelzebub, the enemy of
    our Prince, I here defy him.
Clerk. Let the witnesses appear against the first
    prisoner.
            [*Envy, Superstition, and Pickthank come
                forward. Envy stands forth to give witness.*
Envy. My lord, I have known this man a long
    time, and will attest upon my oath before this
    honourable bench, that he is——
Judge. Hold! give him his oath.
                        [*Envy is handed the oath.*

Envy. [*Reading the oath.*] I swear before Beelzebub and all his Angels. [*Proceeding.*] My
lord, this man is one of the vilest men in our
country, he neither regardeth prince nor people,
law nor custom, but doth all that he can to
possess all men with certain of his disloyal
notions, which he in the general calls principles
of faith and holiness. And in particular,
I heard him once myself affirm, "That Christianity and the customs of our town of Vanity,
were diametrically opposite, and could not be
reconciled." By which saying, my lord, he
doth at once, not only condemn all our laudable
doings, but us in the doing of them.

Judge. Hast thou any more to say?

Envy. My lord, I could say much more, only
I would not be tedious to the court. Yet if
need be, when the other gentlemen have given
in their evidence, rather than anything shall
be wanting that will despatch him, I will
enlarge my testimony against him.

Clerk. Stand by.

Mr. Superstition! Look upon the prisoner.
What can you say for your lord the king
against him?

[*Mr. Superstition is handed the oath and reads
it aloud.*]

Superstition. [*Proceeding.*] My lord, I have no
great acquaintance with this man, nor do

I desire to have further knowledge of him, however, this I know, that he is a very pestilent fellow, from some discourse that the other day I had with him in this town; for then talking with him, I heard him say that our religion was naught, and such by which a man could by no means please God; which sayings of his, my lord, your lordship very well knows, what necessarily thence will follow, to wit, that we still do worship in vain, are yet in our sins, and finally shall be damned. And this is that which I have to say.

Clerk. Mr. Pickthank! [*Handing him the oath.*] Say what you know on behalf of your king against the prisoner at the bar.

Pickthank. [*Reads the oath aloud, and proceeds.*] My lord, and you gentlemen all, this fellow I have known of a long time, and have heard him speak things that ought not to be spoke. For he hath railed on our noble Prince Beelzebub, and hath spoke contemptibly of his honourable friends, with all the rest of our nobility; and he hath said moreover, that if all men were of his mind, if possible, there is not one of these noblemen should have any longer a being in this town. Besides, he hath not been afraid to rail on you, my lord, who are now appointed to be his judge, calling you an ungodly villain, with many other suchlike

vilifying terms, with which he hath bespattered most of the gentry of our town.

Judge. [*To Faithful.*] Thou runagate, heretic, and traitor, hast thou heard what these honest gentlemen have witnessed against thee?

Faith. May I speak a few words in my own defence?

Judge. Sirrah, sirrah, thou deservest to live no longer, but to be slain immediately upon the place, yet that all men may see our gentleness towards thee, let us see what thou hast to say.

Faith. I say then in answer to what Mr. Envy hath spoken, I never said aught but this, "That what rule, or laws, or custom, or people, were flat against the Word of God, are diametrically opposite to Christianity." As to the second, to wit, Mr. Superstition, and his charge against me, I said only this, "That in the worship of God there is required a divine faith." As to what Mr. Pickthank hath said, I say, that the Prince of this town, with all the rabblement his attendants, are more fit for a being in hell, than in this town and country. And so the Lord have mercy upon me.

Judge. Gentlemen of the jury, you see this man about whom so great an uproar hath been made in this town. You have also heard what these worthy gentlemen have witnessed against him. Also you have heard his reply

*G

and confession. It lieth now in your breasts
to hang him, or save his life, but yet I think
meet to instruct you into our law.

There was an act made in the days of Pharaoh
the Great, that lest those of a contrary religion
should multiply and grow too strong for him,
their males should be thrown into the river.
There was also an act made in the days of
Nebuchadnezzar the Great, that whoever would
not fall down and worship his golden image,
should be thrown into a fiery furnace. There
was also an act made in the days of Darius,
that whoso called upon any God but him,
should be cast into the lion's den. Now the
substance of these laws this rebel has broken,
not only in thought—which is not to be borne
—but also in word and deed, which must therefore needs be intolerable, and for the treason
he hath confessed, he deserveth to die the death.

[*Jury gather together in a corner of the court.*

Foreman: Mr. Blind-man. I see clearly that this
man is a heretic.

Mr. No-good. Away with such a fellow from the
earth.

Mr. Malice. Ay, for I hate the very looks of him.

Mr. Love-lust. I could never endure him.

Mr. Live-loose. Nor I, for he would always be
condemning my way.

Mr. Heady. Hang him, hang him.

Mr. High-mind. A sorry scrub!

Mr. Enmity. My heart riseth against him.

Mr. Lyar. He is a rogue.

Mr. Cruelty. Hanging is too good for him.

Mr. Hate-light. Let's despatch him out of the way.

Mr. Implacable. Might I have all the world given me, I could not be reconciled to him, therefore let us forthwith bring him in guilty of death.

Foreman. [*Jury coming forward.*] We find prisoner guilty of death, my lord.

Judge. [*Putting on black cap, and turning to Faithful.*] Then hear your judgment. You shall be scourged, then buffeted, then lanced with knives, after that stoned with stones, then pricked with swords, and last of all burned to ashes at the stake. [*To gaoler.*] Back with them both to prison. Remand the other prisoner until three days' end.

[*Court rises.*

CURTAIN

ACT III

SCENE I

By-path Meadow.

Darkness, thunder, and lightning. Enter Christian and Hopeful.

Chr. What a mercy had you not met me, then had you not been led out of the way on this angry night! Oh! that I had never escaped out of my prison! A thousand fools, I! Yet who could have thought that this path should have led us out of the way?

Hopeful. I was afraid on't at very first, and therefore gave you that gentle caution. I would have spoke plainer, but that you are older than I.

Chr. Good brother, be not offended. I am sorry I have brought thee out of the way, and that I have put thee into such eminent danger. Pray, my brother, forgive me; I did not do it of an evil intent.

Hope. Be comforted, my brother, for I forgive thee; and believe too that this shall be for our good. Rememberest thou not how valiant thou hast been heretofore? Even Apollyon could

not crush thee. What hardship, terror, and amazement hast thou already gone through, and art thou now nothing but fear? Remember how thou playedst the man at Vanity Fair, and wast neither afraid of the chain nor cage, nor yet of bloody death. Bear up. Who knows but He who brought you thence may not once more set our feet on the highway.

Chr. I am glad I have with me a hopeful brother. But we must not stand thus: let's try to go back again.

Hope. But, good brother, let me go before.

Chr. No, if you please, let me go first; that if there be any danger, I may be first therein, because by my means we are both gone out of the way.

Hope. No, you shall not go. The floods are out, and your mind being troubled, may lead you out of the path. [*Leads on, but after a step or two stumbles, and falls, and shouts out.*] Where are we now?

Chr. [*Floundering.*] Nay, I know not. Why, man! Here's a hedge! Let us stay under it till daybreak, or by going on we are like to be drowned.   [*Both lie down as if to sleep.*

CURTAIN

Scene II

Dungeon of the Castle of Giant Despair. Next morning.

Enter Giant Despair with Christian and Hopeful prisoners.

Giant Despair.   Whence do you say you come?

Chr.   We are pilgrims, and journey from the City of Destruction to Mount Zion.

G. D.   What were you doing in my grounds?

Chr.   We had lost our way.

G. D.   You have this night trespassed on my grounds, and therefore you must be cudgelled and lie in this dungeon.

[*Picks up a cudgel, and beats them till they groan in pain on the floor. Giant Despair looks on them with satisfaction.*

Enter Giant Despair's wife, Mrs. Diffidence.

Mrs. Diffidence.   What's all this commotion about?

G. D.   I found these rascals sleeping in the field in By-path Meadow. A lucky thing I got up early!

Diff.   [*To Christian and Hopeful.*]   You dogs! And since you are never like to come out of

this place, your best way would be to make
an end of yourselves. [*To her husband.*] My
dear, bring them knife, halter, and poison.

   [*Exeunt Giant Despair and Mrs. Diffidence.*

Chr. Brother, what shall we do? The life that
we now live is miserable. For my part I know
not whether is best, to live thus, or to die out
of hand. My soul chooseth strangling rather
than life, and the grave is more easy for me
than this dungeon. Shall we be ruled by the
giant?

Hope. Indeed, our present condition is dreadful,
and death would be far more welcome to me
than thus for ever to abide, but others, so far
as I can understand, have been taken by him,
as well as we, and yet have escaped out of his
hand. For my part, I am resolved to pluck
up the heart of a man, and to try my utmost
to get from under his hand. Let's be patient,
and endure awhile; the time may come that
may give us a happy release.

*Enter Giant Despair and Mrs. Diffidence, with
   knife, halter, and poison, which she puts down
   before Christian and Hopeful.   Christian
   swoons for a moment or two.*

Hope. Let us go!
Diff. [*To Giant Despair.*] They are sturdy
rogues. If this does not work, take them into

the castle-yard to-morrow, and show them the bones and skulls of those thou hast already despatched, and make them believe, ere a week comes to an end, thou also wilt tear them in pieces, as thou hast done their fellows before them.

[*Exeunt Giant Despair and Mrs. Diffidence.*

Chr. [*Passionately.*] What a fool am I thus to lie in a stinking dungeon, when I may as well walk at liberty. I have a key in my bosom called Promise, that will, I am persuaded, open any lock in Doubting Castle.

Hope. That's good news. Good brother, pluck it out of thy bosom and try.

Chr. What a blessing he did not search us! [*Tries key in lock.*] Yes, it fits—but the lock goes damnable hard. [*Puts key back in his bosom.*] Once on the king's highway, and we are safe, and out of this giant's jurisdiction. [*Opens door of dungeon slowly; it creaks; the roar of Giant Despair is heard.*] Now for it! Run for your life!   [*Exeunt.*

CURTAIN

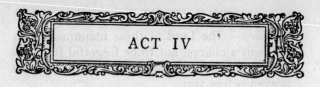

ACT IV

Scene I

The Delectable Mountains.

Enter Christian and Hopeful leaning on rough staves taken from trees. Enter Shepherd from opposite side.

Chr. Well met, friend! Whose delectable mountains are these, and whose be the sheep that feed upon them?

Shepherd. The mountains are Immanuel's Land, and they are within sight of his city, and the sheep also are his.

Enter Second Shepherd. Looks at pilgrims, and gradually draws closer.

Chr. Is this the way to the Celestial City?

First. Shep. You are just in your way.

Chr. How far is it thither?

First Shep. Not too far for you if you are determined to get thither.

Chr. Is the way safe or dangerous?

First Shep. Only transgressors shall fall therein.

Chr. Is there in this place any relief for pilgrims that are weary and faint in the way?

First Shep. The Lord of these mountains hath given us a charge, not to be forgetful to entertain strangers, therefore the good of the place is even before you.

Second Shep. I perceive you are pilgrims. Whence came you?

Chr. From the City of Destruction.

Second Shep. Welcome then to the Delectable Mountains. Thou hast changed a worse for a better. Stay here awhile, to be acquainted with us, and yet more to solace yourselves with the good of these delectable mountains.

Hope. We are well content to stay.

Second Shep. [*To First Shepherd.*] Shall we show these pilgrims some wonders? [*First Shepherd nods assent. To Christian and Hopeful.*] Look afar off. What see you?

Hope. [*Slowly.*] I see as it were several men walking up and down among tombs, and the men stumble as if they were blind.

Chr. What means this?

Second Shep. Did you not see a little below these mountains a stile that led into a meadow on the left hand of this way?

Chr. and Hope. [*Looking at one another.*] Yes.

Second Shep. From that stile there goes a path that leads directly to Doubting Castle, which is kept by Giant Despair, and these men among the tombs came once on pilgrimage, as you do

now, even till they came to that same stile.
And because the right way was rough in that
place, they chose to go out of it into that
meadow, and there were taken by Giant
Despair, and cast into Doubting Castle, where,
after they had been kept awhile in the dungeon,
he at last did put out their eyes, and led them
among those tombs, where he has left them to
wander to this very day.

[*Christian and Hopeful look at one another
and then hide their faces from the shepherds,
as if in shame.*

Chr. Let us go on.

First Shep. Nay, not yet. Look through our
perspective glass.

[*Drawing telescope from wallet. Christian
puts it up to his eyes with trembling
hands, and then passes it to Hopeful.*

[*To Christian.*] What did you see?

Chr. My hands were trembling with the remembrance of the last thing you showed me, but
yet I thought I saw something like a shining
gate.

Hope. [*Bursting out, with glass to eye.*] Brother,
it is the Celestial City. Let us on!

[*Gives back glass hurriedly, and pulls Christian,
as if to go.*

First Shep. [*To Christian.*] Here is a map of
the way. [*Hands map.*

Hope. [*To Christian.*] Come, be brisk.

Chr. [*To Hopeful.*] Bide a while. Thou art like one upon whose head is the shell to this very day.

Hope. Why art thou so tart, my brother?

Chr. [*To First Shepherd.*] Without doubt, sir, 'twill be helpful.

Second Shep. God speed you both!

> [*Exeunt Hopeful followed by Christian, Shepherds looking after them smiling.*

CURTAIN

SCENE II

Before the gate of the Celestial City.

Enter Christian and Hopeful.

Hope. We are pretty near now, judging from the brightness of this place.

> *Enter from opposite side two men in bright golden raiment.*

First Man. Whence come you?

Chr. From the City of Destruction.

Second Man. And you have overcome all the

difficulties and dangers you have met in the way?

Chr. Yes.

First Man. You have loved our Lord, you may go into the City of Zion, the Paradise of God.

Second Man. Aye, and the beauty and glory of it are inexpressible!

First Man. You have but this gate to pass, and you may look your Redeemer in the face with joy.

    [*Knocks at the gate. Gatekeeper opens the gates from within.*

    [*To gatekeeper.*] These are pilgrims come from the City of Destruction, for the love that they bear to the King of this place.

Gatekeeper. Where are their certificates?

First Man. [*To Christian and Hopeful.*] Give him your certificates.

Chr. Faith, I'd forgotten that.

                    [*Fumbles for his roll.*

Hope. I've got mine somewhere, if I can only find it. [*Fumbles.*] Here it is!

Chr. Aye, and mine too!

    [*Christian produces the roll Evangelist gave him, now torn and tattered, and Hopeful a newer one. They give them to the gatekeeper.*

Gatekeeper. I will take these to the King.

        [*Goes within, shutting gates after him.*

Hope. What must we do in the Holy Place?

Second Man. You shall there receive the comfort of all your toil, and have joy for all your sorrow and suffering for the King by the way. You shall enjoy perpetual vision of the Holy One, for there you shall see him as he is. And you shall serve him continually with praise, with shouting and thanksgiving, whom you desired to serve in the world, though with much difficulty.

[*Gatekeeper flings gates wide open from within.*

Gatekeeper. Enter ye into the joy of your Lord.

[*Christian and Hopeful go in, led by the two men. Sound of music as the gates close after them and the curtain drops.*

(Suitable music: *Hallelujah Chorus*; anthem, *Blessing and Honour and Glory and Power*; *Holy, Holy, Holy, Lord God Almighty*; *Doxology*, or some similar hymn of praise.)

CURTAIN

PART II

CHARACTERS

CHRISTIANA.
MATTHEW
SAMUEL
JOSEPH } *her four sons.*
JAMES
VISITOR.

MRS. TIMOROUS.
MERCY.

THE KEEPER OF THE WICKET GATE.

PORTER OF THE HOUSE BEAUTIFUL.
MR. GREATHEART.
DR. SKILL.
LADY OF THE HOUSE BEAUTIFUL.

GIANT MAUL.
MR. HONEST.

MAN IN FLIGHT FROM ROBBERS.
MR. VALIANT-FOR-TRUTH.

TWO CITIZENS.

PART II

ACT I

Scene I

Interior of Christiana's house.

Christiana and her four boys seated at table, having just finished breakfast. A loud knock on the door is heard.

Christiana. If thou comest in God's name, come in.

Enter Visitor. Children chatter together, looking askance at him.

Visitor. Amen. Peace be to this house.
Christiana, knowest thou wherefore I am come?

Chris. [*Trembling.*] No. What is your errand?

Visitor. I dwell with those that are high. It is talked of where I dwell, as if thou hadst a desire to go thither: also there is a report that thou art aware of the evil thou hast formerly done to thy husband in hardening of thy heart against his way, and in keeping of these thy boys in their ignorance. [*Boys look up.*]

217

Christiana, the Merciful One has sent me to tell thee that he is a God ready to forgive, and that he taketh delight to multiply to pardon offences. He also would have thee know that he inviteth thee to come into his presence. [*Christiana bows.*] Christiana! Here is also a letter for thee which I have brought from thy husband's King.

Chris. [*Reading.*] "The King would have you do as did Christian your husband, for that is the way to come to his city, and to dwell in his presence with joy for ever." [*Loudly and imploringly.*] Sir, will you carry me and my children with you, that we also may go and worship this King?

Visitor. Christiana! The bitter is before the sweet. Thou must through troubles, as did he that went before thee, enter this Celestial City. Wherefore I advise thee, to do as did Christian thy husband. Go to the Wicket Gate yonder, over the plain, for that stands in the head of the way up which thou must go, and I wish thee all good speed. Also I advise that thou put this letter in thy bosom. [*Giving a thick letter.*] That thou read therein to thyself and to thy children, until you have got it by root-of-heart. Thou must also deliver it in at the further gate. May you come there with rejoicing. Farewell.

Chris. This is a good day for me. God's blessing
go with you.   [*Exit Visitor.*
[*To her children.*] Come, my children, let us
pack up, and be gone to the gate that leads to
the Celestial Country, that we may see your
father, and be with him, and his companions in
peace, according to the laws of that land.
Children. Hurrah!

CURTAIN

SCENE II

*The same. Bag open, garments, etc., laid out ready
to pack. Christiana hurrying about. A knock
at the door is heard.*

Chris. If you come in God's name, come in.

*Enter slowly, as if surprised, Mrs. Timorous
and Mercy.*

Mrs. Timorous. Neighbour, pray what is your
meaning by this?
Chris. I am preparing for a journey.
Tim. For what journey, I pray you?
Chris. Even to go after my good husband.
Tim. I hope not so, good neighbour. Pray, for

your poor children's sakes, do not so unwomanly cast away yourself.

Chris. Nay, my children shall go with me; not one of them is willing to stay behind.

Tim. I wonder in my very heart, what, or who has brought you into this mind.

Chris. Oh, neighbour, knew you but as much as I do, I doubt not but that you would go with me.

Tim. Prithee what new knowledge hast thou got that so worketh off thy mind from thy friends, and that tempteth thee to go nobody knows where?

Chris. I have been sorely afflicted since my husband's departure from me, and I am now as he was then, nothing will serve me but going on pilgrimage. He dwelleth in the presence of the King of the country, and the Prince of the place has also sent for me with promise of entertainment if I shall come to him: his messenger was here even now, and has brought me a letter, which invites me to come. [*Shows letter.*] What now will you say to this?

    [*Mercy, after having read the letter, stands apart as if in thought.*

Tim. [*Flourishing letter.*] Oh, the madness that has possessed thee and thy husband, to run yourselves upon such difficulties! You have heard, I am sure, what your husband did meet

with, how he met with Apollyon, and many other things. Nor is the danger that he met with at Vanity Fair to be forgotten by thee. For if he, though a man, was so hard put to it, what canst thou, being but a poor woman, do? Consider also thy four sweet boys, thy flesh and thy bones. Wherefore, though thou shouldest be so rash as to cast away thyself, yet for the sake of the fruit of thy body, keep thou at home.

Chris. Tempt me not, my neighbour. I should be a fool of the greatest size, if I should have no heart to strike in with the opportunity. And for that you tell me of all these troubles that I am like to meet with in the way, they are so far off from being to me a discouragement, that they shew I am in the right. The bitter must come before the sweet, and that also will make the sweet the sweeter. Wherefore since you came not to my house in God's name, as I said, I pray you to be gone, and not to disquiet me farther.

Tim. Come, neighbour Mercy, let's leave her in her own hands, since she scorns our counsel and company. [*Mercy hesitates.*

Mercy. Neighbour, I did indeed come with you to see Christiana this morning, and since she is, as you see, a-taking of her last farewell of her country, I think to walk, this sun-shine

morning, a little way with her to help her on the way.

Tim. Well, I see you have a mind to go a-fooling too, but take heed in time, and be wise: while we are out of danger we are out, but when we are in, we are in.   [*Exit, slamming door.*

Chris. Mercy, I take this as an unexpected favour, that thou shouldest set foot out of doors with me to accompany me a little in my way.

Mercy. If I thought it would be to purpose to go with you, I would never go near the town any more.

Chris. Well, Mercy, cast in thy lot with me. I well know what will be the end of our pilgrimage. My husband is where he would not but be, for all the gold in the Spanish mines. Nor shalt thou be rejected, though thou goest but upon my invitation. Besides, if thou wilt, I will hire thee, and thou shalt go along with me as my servant. Yet we will have all things in common betwixt thee and me. Only go along with me.

Mercy. But how shall I be ascertained that I also shall be entertained? Had I this hope, but from one that can tell, I would make no stick at all, but would go being helped by him that can help, though the way was never so tedious.

Chris. Well, loving Mercy, I will tell thee what
thou shalt do. Go with me to the Wicket
Gate, and there I will further inquire for thee,
and if there thou shalt not meet with encouragement, I will be content that thou shalt return
to thy place. I also will pay thee for thy
kindness which thou shewest to me and my
children in thy accompanying of us in our way
as thou doest.

Mercy. Then will I go thither, and will take
what shall follow, and the Lord grant that my
lot may there fall even as the King shall have
his heart upon me.

CURTAIN

ACT II

Summer Parlour at the Wicket Gate.

Enter Christiana and Mercy.

Chris. O Lord! How glad am I that we are got in hither! I thought, one time, as I stood at the gate, because I had knocked and none did answer, that all our labour had been lost, specially when that ugly cur made such a heavy barking against us. [*They sit down.*

Mercy. But my worst fears was after I saw that you were taken into his favour, and that I was left behind. "Now," thought I, "'tis fulfilled which is written, 'Two women shall be grinding together, the one shall be taken, and the other left.'" I had much ado to forbear crying out, "Undone, undone!"

And afraid I was to knock any more, but when I looked up to what was written over the gate—"Knock and it shall be opened unto you"—I took courage. I also thought that I must either knock again or die. So I knocked, but I cannot tell how, for my spirit now struggled betwixt life and death.

Chris. Can you not tell how you knocked? I am sure your knocks were so earnest, that the very sound of them made me start; I thought I never heard such knocking in all my life. I thought you would 'a come in by violent hands, or 'a took the kingdom by storm.

Mercy. Alas, to be in my case, who that so was, could but 'a done so? You saw that the door was shut upon me, and that there was a most cruel dog thereabout. Who, I say, that was so faint-hearted as I, that would not 'a knocked with all their might? But pray, what said the keeper to my rudeness? was he not angry with me?

Chris. When he heard your lumbering noise, he gave a wonderful innocent smile. I believe what you did pleased him well enough, for he shewed no sign to the contrary. But I marvel in my heart why he keeps such a dog. Had I known that afore, I fear I should not have had heart enough to have ventured myself in this manner. But now we are in, we are in, and I am glad with all my heart.

Mercy. I will ask, if you please, next time he comes down, why he keeps such a filthy cur in his yard. I hope he will not take it amiss.

Chris. Ay do. And persuade him to hang him if you like, for I am afraid he will bite us when we go hence.

H

Enter the Keeper of the Gate.

Keeper. Peace be to thee.

Mercy. Wherefore dost thou keep so cruel a dog in thy yard, at the sight of which, such women and children as we are ready to fly from thy gate for fear?

Keeper. That dog has another owner, he also is kept close in another man's ground, only my pilgrims hear his barking. He belongs to the Castle which you see there at a distance, but can come up to the walls of this place. He has frighted many an honest pilgrim from worse to better by the great voice of his roaring. Indeed, he that owneth him doth not keep him of any good will to me or mine, but with intent to keep the pilgrims from coming to me, and that they may be afraid to knock at this gate for entrance. Sometimes also he has broken out, and has worried some that I love, but I take all at present patiently. I also give my pilgrims timely help. But what! I trow, hadst thou known never so much beforehand, thou wouldst not 'a been afraid of a dog. Why! Beggars, that go from door to door, will, rather than they will lose a supposed alms, run the hazard of the bawling, barking, and biting too of a dog. And shall a dog, a dog in another man's yard, a dog whose barking I turn to

the profit of pilgrims, keep any from coming to me?

Mercy. I confess I spake what I understood not.

Chris. Shall we now walk on our way, for we have the weather very comfortable to us?

Keeper. Come a little way with me, and I will tell you of the way you must go. You have only to look before you. It is as straight as a rule can make it as far as the house of the Interpreter, and thence Mr. Greatheart will be your guide; but beware of the many crooked ways that abut down upon it.

CURTAIN

SCENE II

Room in the House Beautiful.

Enter Porter, Greatheart, Christiana, Mercy, and the four boys.

Porter. Ah, Mr. Greatheart! I knew your voice before I opened. But how now! What is your business here so late to-night?

Greatheart. I have brought these pilgrims hither, where by my Lord's commandment, they must lodge. I had been here some time ago, had

I not been opposed by the giant that did use
to back the lions. But I, after a long and
tedious combat with him, have cut him off,
and have brought the pilgrims hither in safety.

[*Matthew here bends double, holding his stomach
as if in pain, and continues to show signs
of pain.*

Porter. Will you not stay till morning?

Greath. No, I will return to my Lord to-night.

Chris. Oh, sir! I know not how to be willing
you should leave us in our pilgrimage, you have
been so faithful, and so loving to us, you have
fought so stoutly for us, you have been so
hearty in counselling of us, that I shall never
forget your favour towards us.

Mercy. O that we might have thy company to
our journey's end! How can such poor women
as we hold out in a way so full of troubles as
this way is, without a friend and defender?

James. Pray sir, be persuaded to go with us,
and help us, because the way is so dangerous
as it is.

Greath. I am at my Lord's commandment. If
he shall allot me to be your guide quite
thorough, I will willingly wait upon you. But
here you failed at first, for when he bid me come
thus far with you, then you should have begged
me of him to have gone quite thorough with
you, and he would have granted your request.

Chris. [*Noticing Matthew in pain.*] Art thou sick?

Matthew. I am torn as 'twere in pieces.

Chris. Where art thou pained?

Matt. In my bowels.

Chris. We must send for a doctor. 'Tis sore upon him.

Greath. There dwells not far from hence one Mr. Skill, an ancient and well approved physician, and——

Chris. Oh, sir! Send at once, that we may know what to do.

Greath. I will go on my way back and desire him to come at once. And so good Christiana, Mercy and my brave children, adieu.   [*Exit.*

Chris. [*Calling after him.*] Pray Mr. Interpreter to send you back to us.

Porter. [*Having shut door after Greatheart.*] The boy is sick of the gripes. Never fear. He will soon do well in the hands of Dr. Skill. But make yourself known to me. What is your country and your kindred?

Chris. [*Still looking at Matthew.*] I came from the City of Destruction. I am a widow woman, and my husband is dead. His name was Christian the pilgrim.

Porter. How, was he your husband?

Chris. Yes, and these are his children. And this—[*Pointing to Mercy.*]—is one of my towns-women.

Porter. I will tell it within that Christiana, the
wife of Christian, and her children, are come
hither on pilgrimage.   [*Exit.*

Chris. I pray the doctor be in, and that he be
not abed.   [*Knock is heard.*
[*Rushing to open door.*] Here he is!

Enter Dr. Skill.

O Doctor, glad am I you are come!

Dr. Skill. Which is the patient?

Chris. Matthew—this one here.

Skill. [*Looking at Matthew.*] Em! [*After a pause.*]
Put out your tongue. [*To Chris.*] What diet
has Matthew of late fed upon?

Chris. Nothing but that which is wholesome.

Skill. This boy has been tampering with something that lies in his maw undigested, and that
will not away without means. And I tell you
he must be purged, or else he will die.

Samuel. Mother, Mother, what was that which
my brother did gather up and eat, so soon as
we were come from the gate that is at the head
of this way? You know that there was an
orchard on the left hand, on the other side of
the wall, and some of the trees hung over the
wall, and my brother did plash and eat.

Chris. True, my child, he did take thereof and
did eat. Naughty boy as he was, I did chide
him, and yet he would eat thereof.

Skill. I knew he had eaten something that was not wholesome food. And that food, to wit, that fruit is even the most hurtful of all. It is the fruit of Beelzebub's orchard. I do marvel that none did warn you of it: many have died thereof.   [*Christiana begins to cry.*

Enter Lady of the House.

Lady. Welcome Christiana, welcome thou wife of that good man, welcome with all—— But what have we here?
              [*Mercy takes her aside and talks with her.*
Chris. O naughty boy, and O careless mother! What shall I do for my son?
Skill. Come, do not be too much dejected. The boy may do well again, but he must purge and vomit.
Chris. Pray sir, try the utmost of your skill with him, whatever it costs.
              [*Mercy speaks aside with the three boys.*
Skill. Nay, I hope I shall be reasonable. I will give him a potion—a strong potion.
    [*Gets a bottle from his bag, and pours potion into a medicine-glass.*
Mercy. [*To the three boys.*] It is not suitable you should remain, and I cannot have you stay up all night.
        [*Exeunt boys with the Lady of the House and Mercy.*

Skill. He must have some now, and take it three times a day. [*Gives it to Matthew, who tastes it, and is loth to take it.*] Come, come, you must take it.

Matt. It goes against my stomach.

Chris. I must have you take it.

Matt. I shall vomit it up again.

Chris. Pray sir, how does it taste?

Skill. It has no ill taste. [*Christiana tastes it.*]

Chris. Oh, Matthew! This potion is sweeter than honey. If thou lovest thy mother, if thou lovest thy brothers, if thou lovest Mercy, if thou lovest thy life, take it.

Matt. [*Gulping it down.*] It goes hard.

Skill. It will cause him to purge: then, put him to bed, and it will cause him to sleep and rest quietly, and will put him into a fine heat and breathing sweat, and quite rid him of his gripes.

Chris. Sir, what will content you for your pains, and care of my child?

Skill. You must pay the Master of the College of Physicians, according to rules made in that case and provided.

Chris. But sir, what is this potion good for else?

Skill. It is an universal potion. 'Tis good against all diseases that pilgrims are incident to, and when it is well prepared, it will keep good, time out of mind.

Chris. Pray sir, make me up another bottle, for if I can get this, I will never take other physic.

Skill. I dare stand to it that this potion is good to prevent diseases, as well as to cure when one is sick. But good Christiana, thou must give it in no other way but as I prescribe, for if you do, it will do no good. [*Preparing to go.*] Now Matthew, take heed how you eat any more green plums.

CURTAIN

SCENE III

Valley of the Shadow of Death.   Very dark at first, gradually getting lighter.

Enter Greatheart, the four boys, Christiana, and Mercy.

Joseph.   Are we not yet at the end of this doleful place?

Samuel.   I am down.

Matt.   Ho!   Where are you?

James.   Alas, now what shall we do?

Greath.   Fear not; stand still, and look to your feet.   'Twill grow lighter ere long.

*H

Mercy. There is not such pleasant being here as at the Gate, or at the Interpreter's, or at the House where we lay last.

Samuel. Oh, but it is not so bad to go through here, as it is to abide here always, and for aught I know, one reason why we must go this way to the house prepared for us, is that our home may be made the sweeter to us.

Greath. Well said, Samuel, thou hast now spoke like a man! For my part, as I have told you already, I have gone often through this valley, and have been much harder put to it than now I am, and yet you see I am alive.

Samuel. Why, if ever I get out here again, I think I shall prize light, and good way better than ever I did in all my life.

Greath. We shall be out by and by.

Joseph. But cannot we see to the end of this valley as yet?

Greath. Be of good courage, and look well to your feet.

Chris. Now I see what my poor husband went through.

Greath. You cannot imagine how many are killed here about, and yet men are so foolishly venturous, as to set out lightly on pilgrimage, and to come without a guide. Poor Christian, it was a wonder that he here escaped!

Chris. Methinks I see something yonder upon

the road before us, a thing of such a shape
such as I have not seen.

> [*Greatheart looks, and draws his sword.*

Joseph. Mother, what is it?

Chris. An ugly thing, child, an ugly thing.

Joseph. But Mother, what is it like?

Chris. 'Tis like I cannot tell what. [*Shrieks.*]
It is nigh!

Greath. Well, well, let them that are most afraid
keep close to me.

Enter Giant Maul, carrying a club.

Maul. Greatheart, how many times have you
been forbidden to do these things?

Greath. What things?

Maul. What things! You know what things.
But I will put an end to your trade.

Greath. But pray, before we fall to it, let us
understand wherefore we must fight.

> [*The pilgrims retire behind Greatheart, at a
> safe distance.*

Maul. You rob the country, and rob it with
the worst of thefts.

Greath. These are but generals, come to parti-
culars, man!

Maul. Thou practisest the craft of a kidnapper,
thou gatherest up women and children and
carriest them into a strange country, to the
weakening of my master's kingdom.

Greath. I am a servant of the God of Heaven. My business is to persuade sinners to repentance. I am commanded to do my endeavour to turn men, women, and children, from darkness to light, and from the power of Satan to God, and if this be indeed the ground of thy quarrel, let us fall to it as soon as thou wilt.

[*They fight. The giant forces Greatheart down to his knees with a blow from his club. The pilgrims cry out in fear. Greatheart recovers himself, wounds the giant in the arm, and both draw back to opposite sides of the stage. They fall to again, and Greatheart fetches the giant to the ground.*

Maul. Nay, hold, and let me recover.

[*Greatheart lets him get up. They fall to again. Greatheart kills Maul, and the pilgrims cheer.*

Matt. Let me look at him.

[*Boys gather round the dead body.*

Chris. Have you caught no hurt in the battle?

Greath. No, save a little on my flesh.

James. But was you not afraid, good sir, when you see him come out with his club?

Samuel. But what did you think when he fetched you down to the ground at the first blow?

[*Greatheart shrugs his shoulders.*

Matt. When you have all thought what you

please, I think God has been wonderful good
unto us in delivering us out of the hand——

Enter Honest, rushing in with drawn sword.

Honest. Who are you? And what is your
business here?

Greath. Come man, be not so hot, here is none
but friends.

Honest. Answer me. What are you?

Greath. My name is Greatheart. I am the guide
of these pilgrims who are going to the Celestial
Country.

Honest. I cry you mercy. I fear'd that you
had been of the company of those that some
time ago did rob Little-faith of his money;
but now I look better about me, I perceive
you are honester people.

Greath. Why, what would, or could you 'a done,
to 'a helped yourself, if we indeed had been of
that company?

Honest. Done! Why, I would 'a fought as long
as breath had been in me, and had I so done,
I am sure you could never have given me the
worst on't.

Greath. Well said, for by this I know thou art
a cock of the right kind. Now we are so
happily met, pray let me crave your name,
and the name of the place you came from.

Honest. I came from the town of Stupidity. It

lieth about four degrees beyond the City of Destruction.

Greath. Oh! Are you that countryman then? I deem I have half a guess of you. Your name is old Honest, is it not?

Honest. Honest is my name. But sir, how could you guess my name?

Greath. I had heard of you before.

Honest. I am forgetting your pilgrims. What are their names?

Chris. My name I suppose you have heard of. Good Christian was my husband, and these four——

Honest. [*Jumping for joy.*] A thousand good wishes! [*Kisses her hand.*] I have heard much of your husband, and of his travels and wars which he underwent in his days. Be it spoken to your comfort, the name of your husband rings all over these parts of the world. His faith, his courage, his enduring, and his sincerity under all, has made his name famous. And these are his four boys? What are their names?

Chris. Matthew, Samuel, Joseph, and James.

Honest. They take all after their father.

Chris. [*Pointing to Mercy, who has drawn back.*] And this maid left town and kindred to come along with us. Mercy is her name.

Honest. Mercy is thy name. [*Kisses her hand.*]

And how hast thou fared since thou set out on pilgrimage?

Mercy. [*Shyly.*] Very well.

Greath. [*To Honest.*] Did you know one Mr. Fearing that came on pilgrimage?

Honest. Know him! I was a great companion of his.

Greath. I was his guide from my master's house to the gates of the Celestial City.

Honest. Then you knew him to be a troublesome one.

Greath. I did so; but I could very well bear it, for men of my calling are oftentimes entrusted with the conduct of such as he was.

Honest. [*Taking Greatheart's arm.*] Well then, as we walk along together, let us hear a little of him, and how he managed himself under your conduct.

CURTAIN

SCENE IV

A path on the Delectable Mountains.

Enter Greatheart and Honest. Enter from opposite side of stage a man running.

Man. [*Hurriedly.*] Gentlemen, if you love life, shift for yourselves, for the robbers are before you.   [*Exit running.*

Greath. Robbers hereabout? They be the three
that set upon Little-faith heretofore. Well, we
are ready for them. [*Draws his sword.*

Honest. I will fight so long as I can hold my
sword in my hand.

Greath. One cometh alone.

Honest. I know this man.

*Enter Valiant-for-Truth, his sword drawn, and
covered with blood.*

Greath. Stand! What art thou?

Valiant. I am one whose name is Valiant-for-
Truth. I am a pilgrim, and am—— Ho!
Father Honest, are you there? Right glad
am I that I have found you on this road. As
I was in my way, there were three men did
beset me, and propounded unto me these three
things: whether I would become one of them,
or go back from whence I came, or die upon the
place. [*Sinks down on the floor. Greatheart
makes him comfortable.*] To the first I answered
I had been a true man a long season, and therefore it could not be expected that I now should
cast in my lot with thieves. Then they de-
manded what I would say to the second. So
I told them that the place from whence I came,
had I not found incommodity there, I had not
forsaken it at all, but finding it altogether
unsuitable to me, and very unprofitable for

me, I forsook it for this way.   Then they
asked me what I said to the third, and I told
them my life cost more dear far than that I
should lightly give it away.   Besides, you have
nothing to do thus to put things to my choice,
wherefore at your peril be it, if you meddle.
Then these three drew upon me, and I also
drew upon them.

Greath.   But here was great odds, three against
one!

Valiant.   'Tis true, but I have read in some
records that one man has fought an army, and
how many did Sampson slay with the jaw-bone
of an ass?

Greath.   Why did you not cry out, that some
might 'a come in for your succour?

Valiant.   So I did.

Greath.   Thou hast worthily behaved thyself.
Let me see thy sword.   Ha!   It is a right
Jerusalem blade.

Valiant.   It is so.   Let a man have one of these
blades, with a hand to wield it, and skill to use
it, and he may venture upon an angel with
it.   He need not fear its holding, if he can
but tell how to lay on.   Its edges will never
blunt.   It will cut flesh, bones, and all.

Greath.   But you fought a great while!   I wonder
you was not weary.

Valiant.   I fought till my sword did cleave to

my hand, and when they were joined together, as if a sword grew out of my arm, and when the blood ran thorough my fingers, then I fought with most courage.

Greath. Thou hast done well. Thou shalt abide by the company I am now taking to the Celestial City, and be their companion. They are even now refreshing themselves with the Shepherds of these Delectable Mountains.

Enter Christina and Mercy, walking slowly. Mercy starts her speech just before actually appearing on the stage.

Mercy. I think I am as well on these mountains as I have been anywhere else in all our journey. The place methinks suits with my spirit. I love to be in such places, where there is no rattling with coaches, nor rumbling with wheels——

Chris. What meaneth this!

Greath. You see how full of dangers is the road. This our companion has been beset by thieves.

Chris. Art thou wounded?

Valiant. I am so, but can make a pretty good shift to wag along.

Chris. We have found entertainment with shepherds, who will wash your wounds, and give you what they have, to refresh you before you go on.

Valiant. I promise you I'll stay. But these wounds are as so many nothings to me. [*Gets up. Christiana makes as if to go with him.*] Nay, go not you too. I'll find the way, and am both willing and able to go alone.

                [*Limps off with difficulty.*

Greath. He has a stout heart, and has been badly hurt, but he will soon do well in this climate. Mount Marvel and Mount Innocent are wonderful healthy places. It goes hard with him. I will after.   [*Exit.*

Mercy. Mother, there is a looking-glass of the shepherds' hangs up, off which I cannot take my mind.

Chris. I will mention thy wants to the shepherds, and they will not deny it thee.

Mercy. I am ashamed that these men should know that I longed.

Chris. Nay, it is no shame, but a virtue, to long for such a thing as that.

Mercy. Then, mother, if you please, ask the shepherds if they are willing to sell it.

Chris. With joyful consent, and quickly, for Mr. Greatheart has a mind to be going.

CURTAIN

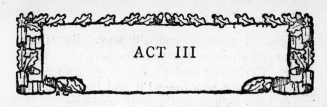

ACT III

Scene I

Street in the Land of Beulah.

Enter two Citizens meeting.

First Cit. More pilgrims are come to town.

Second Cit. Ay, and many went over the water and were let in at the golden gates to-day!

First Cit. Some come, and some go, and I hear there are yet more upon the road.

Second Cit. Who's in Mr. Greatheart's latest company?

First Cit. Hast thou not heard? Why, Christiana, wife of Christian that was, and a townswoman of hers, and three or four swordsmen after Mr. Greatheart's own heart.

Second Cit. I always said Christiana would not be long after her husband.

First Cit. Mr. Greatheart's been a good friend to this town this twenty years.

Second Cit. Yea! None brought so many pilgrims as he. He must be ageing now.

First Cit. But he bears his years well.

Second Cit. I must on. I start betimes in the

morning. I take the boy, and look for the
grey mare.

First Cit.   Loose again?

Second Cit.   Ay!

First Cit.   Broken her tether?

Second Cit.   Ay!   Farewell.

First Cit.   Farewell.   [*Exeunt opposite ways.*

CURTAIN

SCENE II

Room of Christiana's house in the Land of Beulah.
Christiana seated reading.   Knock at door.
Christiana opens.

Enter Greatheart.

Chris.   Good even, Mr. Greatheart!

Greath.   Hail, good woman!   I bring thee tidings
that the Master calleth for thee, and expecteth
that thou shouldest stand in his presence
within this ten days. This shall be thy token:
"An arrow with a point sharpened with love,
let easily into her heart, which by degrees
wrought so effectually with her, that at the
time appointed she must be gone."

Chris. Sir, I would entreat you to have an eye to my children, and if at any time you see them faint, speak comfortably to them.

Greath. Never trust me else!

Chris. [*Going to door and calling.*] Mercy! Mercy!

Greath. I am heartily glad of the news, and could 'a been glad had the post come for me.

Enter Mercy.

Chris. Mercy, my master has need of me, and in very little time I am to behold his face in brightness.

Mercy. I will go with thee.

Greath. Nay, that cannot be, for, to speak plainly, the King doth not want thee till he sends for thee.

Mercy. When think you the King will be willing?

Greath. Nay, I am not acquainted.

Mercy. I will be faithful, and patiently abide.

Greath. [*Rising to go. To Christiana.*] I wish you a fair day when you set out for Mount Zion.

Chris. Sir, I will tell the King with thankfulness of your conduct and deliverance of us. Pray, take this ring from me in remembrance of our journey.

Greath. Glad am I to have brought you in safety hither without reward, but with good will

accept thy ring as token of a happy journey. Ever when I look upon this ring shall I be in mind of thee and of all this band of pilgrims.

Chris.   And so may I live in the light of the living for ever. Farewell night! Welcome day!

CURTAIN.

CURTAIN.

LIFE OF JOHN BUNYAN

JOHN BUNYAN was born at Elstow in Bedford-shire in 1628. His father was a mender of pots and kettles, and later the son followed and increased his father's trade till he became a prosperous brazier and a householder in Bedford. In 1644, when he was sixteen, Bunyan joined the Parliamentary Army and was probably with his regiment till 1647, but we have no record that he saw any severe fighting. He married in 1649 a woman who was a true comrade and helpmate to him for many years. At first they were very poor—" not having so much house-hold stuff as a dish or a spoon between us." The wife had, however, two books, *The Plain Man's Pathway to Heaven*, and *The Practice of Piety*. These the young couple read together.

Bunyan says his youth was desperately evil. He accuses himself of being so terribly wicked that no forgiveness seemed possible. But he was probably only wild and reckless. Because later he set himself so high and noble a standard of conduct and feeling, his early life seemed

sunk in sin. When his conscience became
awakened he lived carefully and tried to do
right, but he was troubled by terrible visions
and thought that God had cast him out from
His presence for ever. For long he suffered such
tremendous agonies of mind that he wished he
might die, and yet feared to die lest he should
be doomed to Hell. At last peace came to him;
he knew in his heart and mind that the love of
Christ for him had made it possible to escape
from the evil of his former life and follow in his
Master's steps—like Christian, at the Cross he
lost his burden. Many troubles and temptations
were still to beset him, but never again did he
despair, for never did he lose the sense of the
love of God as shown in Christ.

In 1653 he joined the Baptist Church in Bedford. His earnestness was known, and the congregation, in 1655, asked him to preach. Bunyan
refused, believing himself unworthy, but at
length " he made experiment of his powers " in
private, and at once his gift was manifest. He
preached what he himself had experienced; he
had a burning fiery faith and men flocked from
all the country round to hear him. " I preached
what I felt, what I smartingly did feel."

But at the Restoration, 1660, Nonconformists
were forbidden to meet together for worship.
Bunyan would not promise to abstain from

preaching and teaching, and he was arrested and imprisoned. For twelve years, 1660-72, he remained a prisoner, probably not all the time under rigorous arrest, but certainly not free to be with his family. During his imprisonment they were helped by members of the congregation, but he himself toiled hard to support them. " I have been witness," writes a friend, " that his own hands ministered to his and his family's necessities, making many hundred gross of long-tagged laces to fill up the vacancies of his time, which he had learned for that purpose since he had been in prison." He could not preach, save occasionally to his fellow prisoners, but what his lips might not say his pen wrote. *Grace Abounding* is the most important of many works written during this period. It is really the story of his own early struggles and temptations, and of the Grace and Love that saved him.

In 1672 Bunyan was freed under the Declaration of Indulgence. But the respite was only for a short time. In 1675 he was imprisoned again—in the jail he refers to as " a den " in the opening of *The Pilgrim's Progress*. And it was most probably during this second imprisonment that he wrote his great allegory. Perhaps it was not quite finished when he was finally released in 1676. It has been suggested that the break in the story which occurs when the

Pilgrims leave the Delectable Mountains has
something to do with this. The paragraph ends,
" So I awoke from my dream," and the next
begins, " And I slept and dreamed again." When
he had finished his book Bunyan was not quite
sure about publishing it. He showed it to friends;
some advised one way, some another:

> Some said, John, print it; others said Not so.
> Some said It might do good; others said No.
> Now was I in a strait and did not see
> Which was the best thing to be done by me.
> At last I thought, Since you are so divided,
> I print it will, and so the case decided.

And *The Pilgrim's Progress* was, happily for us,
published in 1678, and at once was widely read
and loved. Edition after edition was called for.
Its fame went far and wide, and very early it
was translated into many foreign tongues. A
second part appeared in 1685, describing the
journey of Christiana and her children.

Bunyan lived till 1688, preaching and helping
his people in Bedford. He refused offers of
important positions, preferring his work among
the friends he knew and loved. He died in
London on his way back from a visit to reconcile
a father and son who were at enmity, and, his
pilgrimage over, lies buried in Bunhill Fields.

A contemporary has described him: " He
was tall of stature, strong-boned, though not
corpulent; somewhat of a ruddy face, with

sparkling eyes; wearing his hair on his upper lip; his hair reddish, but in his later days time had sprinkled it with grey; his nose well set, but not declining or bending; his mouth moderate large, his forehead somewhat high and his habit always plain and modest." We feel we know him well, because *The Pilgrim's Progress* is largely the story of his own journey to the Celestial City. It is, too, the story of all of us who are wayfaring and warfaring pilgrims, and because he understands the difficulties and dangers that face us, we look upon him as a guide and comrade on our road. He knows not only the difficulties of the way—he knows the happy resting-places. He tells us of the House Beautiful and of the Delectable Mountains as well as of Doubting Castle and the Slough of Despond. He has sympathy and he has humour; above all, he has a compelling faith in the worthwhileness of that journey which has been made possible to each one of us through the Life and Love of the Lord Christ.

SOME SUGGESTED QUESTIONS

1. (a) Bunyan knew the Bible almost by heart.
Select passages from *Pilgrim's Progress* that especially
show the influence of the Bible on Bunyan's style.

(b) He often uses the everyday expressions of the
people of his time. Give examples.

(c) Was it good to use two styles so different in one
story? Give reasons for your answer.

2. Describe what happened when Christian lost his
burden.

3. Bunyan often uses minute details to make his
scenes more vivid. Give some examples.

4. Write *Pilgrim's Progress* in the form of a parable.

5. In what respects did the adventures of Christian
up to the time of meeting with Faithful differ from
those of Faithful?

6. Draw a plan of Christian's journey, marking all
important places; *or*, Draw a picture of any incident in
his journey.

7. Describe Vanity Fair; *or*, Tell the story of Little-
faith.

8. Write an allegory—The journey of Youth from
the City of Childhood to the House of Learning.

9. Where did the following live: Mr. Talkative, Mr.

Legality, Pliable, Mr. Worldly Wiseman, Mr. By-ends?
In one or two sentences describe each of these characters.

10. Relate the adventures of Christian and Hopeful
in Doubting Castle. Do you know any story that may
have suggested this scene to Bunyan?

11. Write a brief ballad, or other poem, describing
Christian's fight with Apollyon; *or*, Give a prose account
of it.

12. Describe Christian's crossing of the river, and
his entry into the Celestial City.

A
GOOD·BOOK
· IS THE ·
PRECIOUS
LIFE-BLOOD
· OF A ·
MASTER
SPIRIT
Milton

PRINTED IN   GREAT BRITAIN